THE MODERN ASPECT OF MATHEMATICS

The MODERN ASPECT *of* MATHEMATICS

by

LUCIENNE FÉLIX

Translated by

JULIUS H. HLAVATY

and

FANCILLE H. HLAVATY

Basic Books, INC.

PUBLISHERS

New York

To the memory of my brother
ROGER FÉLIX (1899–1918)
who, at the age of four, discovered
the rule of casting out nines;
who, at the age of seventeen, was a
student at the École Normale
Supérieure;
who, at the age of nineteen, died
for France.

Foreword

Mathematics is alive and growing. This statement may seem paradoxical to those who remember the subject as they studied it in school and think of the hoary symbols which for so many centuries have represented the tools and operations of mathematics: the ten numerical digits; the signs $+$, $-$, $\times$, $\div$, $=$, $<$, and $>$; the handful of further symbols used in the more advanced branches of the study, such as the expressions $\dfrac{dy}{dx}$, Δy, $\Sigma y \, \Delta x$ and $\int y \, dx$ in calculus.

But you have only to look into a modern treatment of mathematics, or indeed into some current engineering journals, to find a strange new language, made up of symbols like these:

(1) $$(p \vee q) \implies (r \Leftrightarrow (s \wedge \smallsmile t));$$

(2) $$\exists x[P_x] \text{ means } P_a \vee P_b;$$

(3) $$\exists x \forall y[x = \sqrt{y^2}\,];$$

(4) $$A \subset B;$$

(5) $$\overline{(A \cup B)} = \overline{A} \cap \overline{B};$$

(6) $$F: x \to y;$$

(7) $$U = \{1, 2, 3, 4, 5\};$$

(8) $$B = \{x \mid x + 4 > 5\};$$

(9) $$A \times A = \{(x, y) \mid (x \in A) \wedge (y \in A)\};$$

(10) $$R - \{(x, y) \mid x \, Ry\}.$$

What does all this mean? It means primarily that the field of mathematics has been enriched in the twentieth century by new, powerful, exciting ideas. The new conceptions are not only interesting creations of the imagination; they are also useful in many fields of work—in science, technology, yes even in the so-called humanistic studies. The versatility of modern mathematics and mathematical logic has made it possible to apply mathematical methods not only in physics and engineering but also in industrial planning, medicine, biochemistry, biophysics, sociology, even in problems of philosophy and linguistics.

The number and variety of mathematical disciplines have greatly increased in the last sixty years. New branches of knowledge based on mathematical methods have been created. Among these can be mentioned: the design of experiments, mathematical population theory, theory of risks, symbolic logic, biomathematics, factor analysis, quality control, the mathematical theory of communication, information theory, the theory of strategy and games, linear programing, periodogramanalysis and time series, and statistical decision theory. Although not all of these new theories have produced practical results commensurate with their mathematical structure, workers in the fields that generated these disciplines are convinced that the mathematical approach has been on the whole beneficial to their particular domains.

Mathematicians themselves are developing new fields of exploration in pure mathematics: axiomatics; abstract algebra, including the theory of groups, rings, fields, and vector spaces; combinatorial topology and algebraic topology; lattice theories; general theory of sets; theory of linear spaces; tensor calculus; and even metamathematics—a study about, not of, mathematics.

These new conceptions have broken up the traditional compartments that housed arithmetic, algebra, and geometry; and the classical treatment of mathematics in school has therefore become in considerable part obsolete.

Just as an informed layman, or a good teacher, must keep abreast of changing points of view in social and cultural relations, in political economy, in the arts, in man's interpretation of his world, so it is imperative that he maintain intellectual contact with the major new developments in science. The nations that lead the world in the coming decades will be those that lead in knowledge, interpretation and use of science. And the basis of all science is a growing body of mathematical knowledge. More and more our search into the unknown is guided by mathematical models.

Modern mathematics is therefore an essential element in modern education. We are indebted to Mademoiselle Félix for giving us in this book an urgently needed elementary explanation of some of the basic ideas in the new approach to the subject. She has done so in a manner that displays mathematics for what it has surely become: an art, a humanity, and the highest of all the sciences.

Mathematics is an art because it creates forms and patterns of pure thought that exhibit the noblest achievement of the human mind. It has become one of the great humanities because it is a method of expressing, explaining and communicating man's total behavior. It still reigns as queen of the sciences in its clear, rigorous, logical structure, and in doing so serves as an ideal and goal for the perfection of other sciences, as researchers in those fields seek to discover the laws of the physical, biological and social phenomena of our universe.

—HOWARD F. FEHR

Introduction

This is not a book *of* mathematics—it is a book *about* mathematics. It will not be welcomed by those who prize precision above all else, who like the finished project where everything is clear and definitive. As mathematical technicians, the precisionists are very skillful; as teachers they have great attributes of clarity and their pupils do well in their courses. But suppose these pupils ask: "How is it that I do not understand?" or perhaps "Now that I have finished the course, why can't I do the problems?" Then the teachers must often think, perhaps even say aloud, "I too, I do not know why."

Other people are less interested in specific statements than in well-built theories, in fruitful ideas, in the logical or even psychological value of relations, in the versatility which makes it possible to obtain—by means of models—representations satisfying our requirements and often useful in various areas. In this state of mind we feel that it is possible to make contact even with mathematics far above our level, mathematics whose power and beauty, even though barely glimpsed, are a fountain of enrichment for the mind, and an opportunity for long reflections on our modest activities as users or teachers of elementary mathematics.

It is to this second category that this book is addressed. The author hopes it will encourage the reader to look into not only the books cited but all the periodicals, all the books within his reach. The reader will find very often that the prefaces, the first two or three pages, are inspiring, that they open up immense horizons of which each reader can explore more or less extended sections, according to his abilities.

Our hopes will be fulfilled if some of our readers feel encouraged to try their strength on exercises they suggest to themselves, or preferably, to study perseveringly some books on a subject they choose. Not only will they enjoy the keen pleasure of an intellectual "sport," but all their scientific or teaching activity will be illuminated.

Contents

Contents

THE MODERN ASPECT OF MATHEMATICS

Mathematicians have never been in full agreement on their science, though it is said to be the science of self-evident verities—absolute, indisputable and definitive. They have always been in controversy over the developing aspects of mathematics, and they have always considered their own age to be a period of crisis.

—HENRI LEBESGUE

THE SCANDAL
IN MATHEMATICS

Is there a scandal in modern mathematics? Mathematics has long been considered a science of certainty. Its method was strictly imposed by its aim: the study of numbers and measures in space (lengths, surfaces, volumes). This method, deduction, reigned as a supreme tyrant in its construction, so that mathematics emerged with the character of absolute certitude—probably the only science beyond the reach of doubt, of skepticism, or of faith. This is still the idea that non-mathematicians have of mathematics. People used to say, and still say, "It is as certain as that two and two make four." If you speak of a revolution in mathematics, you are likely to be treated to the ironic response, "Oh, so two and two now make five?" We can answer: "Why not? Suppose we ask for the delivery of two articles each weighing two pounds; they are delivered in a box weighing one pound; then in this package two pounds and two pounds will make five pounds!"

"But you get five pounds by adding three weights, 2 and 2 and 1."

"True, our operation '2 and 2 make 5' is not an addition in the usual sense. But we can define the operation to make the result hold true. We can imagine a packaging such that the operation might be, for instance:

> 2 and 2 make 5; 2 and 3 make 6 (if the box weighs one pound in each case),
> 3 and 3 make 8; 3 and 4 make 9 (if the box weighs two pounds), etc.

"The symbol 'etc.' here stands for a rule of the game, which would define how much a and b would 'make' for all pairs of integers a and b. We would thus define an operation and we could study its properties."

This answer would undoubtedly seem frivolous to our questioner. It would seem to him to be a game; the study we could make of this game would not seem to be a part of mathematics; besides, we would not have invented anything, for we would merely be thinking of the sum of three terms (of which one was understood), while he was thinking of a real addition of two terms.

Before discussing the fundamental question: "Is our operation a part of mathematics?" we should point out to the dissenter that the form of his question is poor, for "and" is not a synonym for "plus" nor "make" a synonym for "equal." We cannot state anything, understand anything, or above all, criticize anything in mathematics without extreme precision in vocabulary and language.

One of the indisputable characteristics of mathematics is that it is a rigorous language with practically no synonyms. If this ideal is not attained in a particular statement or description, that is an indication of imperfection; the corresponding theory is not yet a part of perfected mathematics, though it may very well be a very important chapter of the science in process of formation. Just as mathematics was not created in one day, so its language could not have been fixed from the first moment of the work of its construction. But an idea which has not been formulated is not a part of the science; mathematical language has been formed step by step, keeping pace with the ideas that had to be expressed and with the logical requirements relating to the connections among these ideas. It is therefore certain, and the history of mathematics gives evidence, that every period of creation is at the same time a period in which the language changes. This evolution of language, of symbolism, of notation, is, so to speak, the external aspect of the evolution of the science, the internal one being a change in the intuitive, psychological and metaphysical state of the creative scholar. To mathematics, even more than to the natural sciences, one can apply Antoine Lavoisier's remark in the introduction to his treatise on *Chemistry:* "Since ideas are preserved and trans-mitted by words, we cannot perfect language without perfecting science, nor science without perfecting language; however certain may be the facts, however accurate may be the ideas that spring from them, they will nevertheless convey only a false impression unless we have exact terminology with which to express them."

Every epoch of great scientific achievement—particularly changes of ideas growing out of re-examination of fundamentals —is marked by a development of language.

A word, by itself, may evoke a mental attitude, even an epoch (for example, *indivisibles, fluxions*), and since a word must be used, its introduction demands an entirely new vocabulary—expressions either new or used with new meanings.

In such areas, naturally, some scientists pursue their work within their customary concepts, which may remain quite valid within the area of their study; they thereby separate themselves from the innovators who break with the traditional framework of thought and who turn the customary patterns upside down. But the interdependence of the various branches of science inevitably causes dissension if scientists cease to understand each other. A crying need is then felt to codify the new doctrine in order to make it comprehensible and transmissible, in the hope that it will be adopted in the future; and this is even more important because the task of unifying and organizing becomes unavoidable. It is rare indeed that one scientist creates a new thought by himself; history teaches that every discovery is, so to speak, "in the air" at a given time, and that it gushes forth simultaneously from the minds of several scientists in similar, incomplete forms. We are well acquainted with such syntheses, with such expositions of the science of a whole epoch. The most famous one is the treatise of Euclid, the result of the attempt to overcome the two great difficulties in the face of which mathematics had failed: the existence of irrational numbers and the uniqueness of the line parallel to a given line through a given point.

The first difficulty was solved, or rather by-passed, in the sixth book (largely due to Eudoxus) by the use of sequences of rational numbers, employing an inspiration which, as we know today, was completely correct. The second difficulty was tentatively set aside by the adoption of a postulate (still called the *postulate of Euclid*) which suggested that some day it would be possible to demonstrate the conclusion in question, or else prove that such a demonstration was impossible. (We know that this impossibility, already a presentiment with such mathematicians as Lambert, was proved by Lobachevsky, Bolyai and Gauss, who constructed non-Euclidean geometries.)

The *Elements* of Euclid, supplemented with such works as Apollonius' *Conics* and Archimedes' *Analysis,* constituted "mathematics" for centuries. Its prestige was so great that teaching is still impregnated with it (perhaps even more in some other countries than in France); every other method is set alongside the Greek thought rather than in place of it. For example, as Henri Lebesgue says, "Decimal notation is not an inheritance from the Greeks; that seemed sufficient reason for everything which derives from that notation to be merely pasted onto the Greek heritage and not incorporated into it. Our teaching does not yet fully use this historic achievement, perhaps the most important in the history of the sciences, the invention of decimal notation."

It is not our intention to give here an exposition of the history of mathematics, nor even to enumerate the writings which, like Euclid's, determined teaching for a time, since they represented the state of science of the period while the science of the future was being worked out. But let us point out, as a warning, the cause of a halt in creative work in France during the second half of the seventeenth century. In the words of René Taton (*History of Calculation,* Series *Que Sais-je?*): "This decline seems due to the inadequacy of our education, which the universities and the colleges of the Jesuits, failing in their task, refused to modernize."

What scandals there have been in this story of mathematics since the scandal of the irrational numbers! Scandals of numbers called fictitious, or false, or even absurd! These—the negative numbers—were introduced by the Hindus and the Arabs, were used by Chuquet (in 1485) to generalize the notion of exponents, but were still not really understood by Descartes (his *Geometry* was written in 1637). We know that Descartes' folium had for him the shape not of a curl with two infinite branches but of a four-leaf clover (whence its name), for positive values of the coordinates were marked in both directions on both axes. There were also the scandals of the imaginaries (complex numbers), of the indivisibles, of the infinitely small, of vanishing quantities, of illusory forms! Doesn't the very terminology show the terror of the mathematicians in the face of their own monstrous creations?

At the end of the seventeenth century it was the scandal of divergent series, which to Abel were "wholly an invention of the devil." This was the era in which the enthusiasm and imagination of the heirs of Newton and Leibniz accumulated the most daring results, trusting to the method expounded in d'Alembert's famous exclamation: "March ahead, and faith will come to you." "The geometers of the eighteenth century, trained in calculations, treating only particular cases, always left to the reader the task of 'performing the same operation' in the cases not treated, and it sometimes happened that they did not foresee the difficulties which one would encounter as soon as he tried to 'perform the same operation'" (Henri Lebesgue, Note on Vandermonde). One wonders what a general exposition of mathematics written by Gauss (1777–1855) would have looked like if the *Disquisitiones Arithmeticae* (1801) had been but a single chapter in it!

But Gauss was one of the first to feel the need for rigor. We can understand why he not only did not write such a treatise, but on the contrary, preserved unpublished his innumerable and powerful discoveries. They were ahead of his time and could have found a place only in a more rigorous and more beautiful construction of mathematics. To Lacroix (1765–1843) goes the credit for attempting such a general exposition in his *Treatise on Differential and Integral Calculus*, prepared as early as 1792. By this work, as well as by his translation of the treatise by Babbage, Peacock and Herschel (1816), he made a great contribution to the improvement of instruction. But it was Cauchy who succeeded in introducing clarity and rigor. He was "forced to accept propositions which may seem a little hard to accept; for example, that a divergent series does not have a sum." He introduced, with precision, the necessary definitions of limit, of convergence, and thus made possible, in a short time, great advances in areas which had been finally clarified.

Another, a most fruitful, century went by. It seemed that at last a satisfactory state had been achieved, even though it was recognized as tentative and perfectible. New treatises appeared and were circulated widely among the students. In the preface to his *Analysis* (1891) Picard wrote: "I am not unaware of the difficulties of the task which I am undertaking. Activity in mathematical thinking today is such that it is perhaps presumptuous to attempt to sketch, in so vast an area, the present state of the science. The portrait, even if it is a good likeness, is fated, in parts at least, to become dated rather quickly. But that does not matter so long as I propose merely to be useful as a guide to those who wish to acquaint themselves with modern analysis and who fear that, alone, they may lose their way in the multiplicity of papers which fill the learned scientific periodicals." Despite the prudence and modesty of Picard's tone, do we not feel a serene confidence in the essentially sure foundations of a science which would change, to be sure, but which would not experience any profound revolution, and whose validity was assured?

It can be said, I believe, that the bible of mathematics, insofar as it concerns analysis, expounded with assurance and without perceptible qualms, was Goursat's treatise. His book, in whole or in part, was the text to study in order to prepare for examinations and to serve one's apprenticeship as a mathematician during the first half of our century. It was perhaps Goursat's personality, and it was certainly pedagogic considerations, that gave the book its positive tone of definitive exposition. The introduction asserted, without hesitation, the foundations of analysis: "From the concept of whole numbers we rise successively to those of rational numbers, of irrational numbers, and of algebraic numbers. We will assume that the reader has already mastered these concepts, and that he knows the theory of algebraic operations and the application of numbers to the measurement of concrete magnitudes." To be sure, a note confesses that it is necessary to be precise, and ends by saying: "To establish this essential point, we must base ourselves on a postulate which is derived from our intuitive knowledge of the straight line. This postulate, moreover, can be expressed in various forms, though equivalent in reality." What postulate? Which forms? The reader is not initiated into these mysteries, which are considered too recondite for him; he will have to be satisfied with intuitive statements like: "It evidently reduces to the same as saying . . ." or "it is clear that all rational numbers are . . ." Warnings, however, indicate the need for prudence, and Cauchy's criteria are repeatedly underlined: "We can see by these examples that it is easy to construct continuous functions which do not have derivatives for certain particular values of the variable. Weierstrass, in 1872, had completely resolved the problem by giving examples of continuous functions which have no derivatives for any values of the variable. Since no applications have yet been found for these functions, we shall not deal with them."

What Goursat, as a teacher, did not wish to emphasize was that while he was describing an imposing monument, subterranean explorers were examining its foundations, raising doubts about its stability and its value in relation to a structure that should include all of mathematics.

Again scandal appeared in mathematics! And this in spite of the refusal to consider certain questions legitimate. Just as Plato had rejected constructions that require more than the straight edge and compass, so Kronecker rejected transcendental numbers. As E. T. Bell reports in *Men of Mathematics*, Kronecker said to Lindemann, who had just demonstrated the transcendence of π (in 1882, after Hermite had demonstrated the same for e in 1873): "What good is your beautiful investigation regarding π? Why study such problems, since irrational [and hence transcendental] numbers do not exist?" And Hermite himself, who had just given the first illustration of transcendental numbers and did not fear them, wrote, when confronted with modern works on the theory of functions: "I turn aside in horror from this lamentable plague of functions which do not have derivatives." He wished, for a while, to oppose the insertion into the *Comptes-Rendus* of the Academy of Sciences of a note by Lebesgue (1899) on non-ruled surfaces which are representable on a plane. Let us quote Lebesgue himself to characterize this resistance to the appearance of new monstrosities: "To many mathematicians, I became the man of the functions without derivatives, although I never at any time gave myself completely to the study or consideration of such functions. And since the fear and horror which Hermite showed was felt by almost everybody, whenever I tried to take part in a mathematical discussion there would always be an analyst who would say, 'This won't interest you; we're discussing functions having derivatives.' Or a geometer would say it in his language: 'We're discussing surfaces that have tangent planes.' " They tried to contain the havoc by admitting that there were no doubt exceptional cases without general significance to be found, but only if one looked for them! But the discontinuous cropped up whenever the conditions of the applications of theorems were made precise. Moreover, if mathematics was to serve physics, it could not recoil before these difficulties.

It therefore became essential to establish the foundations of the theory of sets (which Georg Cantor did in 1874), to enrich it with the necessary concept of the power of a set, to define a metric upon sets, to classify these sets, and to reason about them. This was not easy! Totally unexpected contradictions shook the scientific world (especially from 1895 on) until the enunciation of Zermelo's axiom applied a match to the fuse and divided mathematicians into two enemy camps. Feeling the need for a continuous up-to-date compilation of these discussions, Emile Borel founded the *Collection of*

Monographs on the Theory of Functions. The first monograph was devoted to the *Theory of Sets;* the second edition of 1914 was enriched by the celebrated "Note IV" containing the exchange of letters (1904) among Baire, Borel, Hadamard, and Lebesgue. Since 1914, papers have proliferated. Scattered throughout innumerable journals in all countries, they are the works of an ever-increasing number of scholars of the most diverse tendencies.

But the war of 1914–1918 came and, for France at least, it meant the disappearance of a generation of young people, a halt to the publication and the diffusion of foreign works, and a slowing up of improvements in doctrines of higher education. An evolution more rapid than any that history had ever known took place over the entire world and transformed not only pure science but also its relations with society. Whole new branches were grafted onto classical mathematics as a result of new applications; and the revolutionary theories of relativity and quantum physics required a mathematics adapted to them. Is it any wonder that a schism occurred among the scientists—some pursuing their research in the traditional path, and others creating a new vocabulary, a new symbolism better adapted to the needs of their thinking?

Once again, history repeated itself. After a period of fertile outpouring, a synthesis was called for; but the source was so abundant and so little disposed to stop flowing that the studies seemed more urgent than the synthesis. It was then that a group of young people, still students but already original thinkers and no longer satisfied with Goursat, decided to compose the *Analysis of the New School.* This project was destined to be so expanded as to embrace all of mathematics conceived in its entirety. Thus was begun the new bible of modern mathematics: the *Elements* of Bourbaki. What matter if some of its details of terminology and symbolism are not universally accepted! Present-day scholars, whether or not they accept the label of "Bourbakists," now refer their students to the *Elements* for the introduction to the fundamental concepts which they assume to be known and which they do not wish to deal with in their own treatment. We may therefore consider the Bourbaki treatise to be a complete and coherent exposition of modern mathematics. Mathematicians the world over refer to it in their bibliographies, even if they may prefer a different set of axioms or different expository procedures better adapted to the needs of different readers.

A necessary condition for the validity of such an enterprise is clearly that the science conceived in this new way should sacrifice nothing of the science that has already been established; that lodes of mines already discovered, whether they are active or quiescent, should retain their place in the scheme as areas for exploration. The books of the *Elements* of Bourbaki that have already appeared, and those that are to appear, promise, in effect, to cover the whole domain of mathematics, and the ambition of the authors is to construct a base sufficiently broad to serve as a foundation for the mathematics of the present and of the near future.

Where, then, is the scandal? That some mathematicians pursue their research by traditional paths or paths not in conformity with the Bourbakist codification? Isn't that their right? Or that some technicians insist that future engineers have skills in certain computational and drawing techniques which have little interest for some modern theoreticians? Isn't that their duty, if these techniques are important in their trades? And yet, the scandal does exist. Our generation has seen the emergence of new technicians, devoted to the practical problems that are raised by, for example, electricity, electronics, communications (cybernetics), calculating machines, etc. The users of mathematics demand new mathematical studies, which the researchers ought to be prepared to undertake. Moreover, now that a general conception of the universe has evolved, all educated men, whether or not they are specialists in science, have the right to an explanation which, however elementary, will give them an insight into the new aspects of scientific thought. So the scandal really exists, but it is on the level of teaching, and it is being reduced little by little as necessary adaptations are being made.

It would be scandalous if a student graduating with his first university degree were to learn that what he had been taught did not permit him to continue his studies: if, for example, a medical student ready for specialization found that he was obliged to start studying mathematics from scratch. Similarly it is scandalous when a young graduate is so untutored in modern science that he finds himself two generations behind in attempting to understand the modern world. Let us admit that secondary education must inevitably be one generation behind in science—the generation of the teacher himself. Besides, it takes time to ripen and winnow the latest harvest of science. But when it is a question of elements which have already been integrated into science and which have been taught from the very beginning of higher education, ignorance is no longer permissible. No teacher of mathematics at the secondary level should be ignorant of what his students will be studying the following year in preparing for teaching or for engineering.

The lag is perhaps excusable in France, where the removal of a whole generation has prevented a normal adjustment in our universities. After the generation of the great teachers (Darboux, Appell, Hadamard, Picard—whose students gave their lives for France—and their immediate successors Lebesgue, Borel, Montel, etc.) too few scholars, miraculously escaping the catastrophe, transmitted a living learning. Then, suddenly, there appeared in Paris the young masters whom we now applaud, whose names appear in the reviews and the proceedings, those who along with their friends and rivals have participated in the Bourbakist group. None of this is shocking, but as an instructor in a secondary school said, expressively though colloquially, "Suddenly we found that we had lost control of the steering wheel."

Alarm about these changes is now a thing of the past. There is intense activity in the school world; individual and collective search for a synthesis goes on. All the voices that are heard—some dynamic, others moderate—agree that standing still would be wrong. New books are appearing—textbooks and beginners' books. The needs of the day demand that this process be accelerated.

II

. . . the future will be only more radical and not less, only more strange and not more familiar.

—J. ROBERT OPPENHEIMER

THE TWENTIETH-CENTURY REVOLUTION IN VALUES

All human activity, to be understood, must be considered in its context—its time and place. It is especially the time, more than place, that we consider of importance today, when interpenetration has brought virtual uniformity to all nations in our civilization, particularly in the realm of science.

We cannot isolate mathematicians from their intellectual brethren who, in the arts or in the natural sciences, take part in a whirlwind of activity, constantly reconsidering the very foundations of their thought: the intuitive knowledge of the real world, the deductive movement of reasoning, the possibility of scientific explanations of number and space, the classification of the sciences or of esthetic and moral values. Even a sketchy outline of any intellectual specialty in our century involves comparisons with bordering activities. It is as if, with the disappearance of the universal man (such as Leonardo da Vinci), more or less conscious influences have worked to establish in society as a whole the connection between specialties which formerly could exist within the mind of one man. These influences, so far as thought is concerned, almost always originate in the material contributed by mathematics or physics, and the terms of comparison follow in this order: mathematics, music, painting, poetry.

It is an entertaining and interesting game to substitute mathematical terms in a learned critique of, say, music or painting and note the close parallelism. For instance, take a passage in *Musique Nouvelle,* by Stuckenschmidt: "From the beginning, the requirements of expression [application], though perhaps a doubtful and controversial basis from the point of view of pure music [pure mathematics], have blazed the trail for inventions of harmonic, melodic and structural [algebraic, geometric and structural] order which were also indicated in the law of the development of musical notation [the architecture of mathematics]; from these came the blossoming of the traditional forms of the sixteenth century and, similarly, of the forms of three centuries later. People thought they saw jokes, grotesque deviations from the norm, but these bits of apparent nonsense actually proceeded from a rigorous, logical process which was to give rise to quite serious developments."

A bird's eye view of the evolution of music and painting will help us to understand better, to accept more readily as a human necessity, the transformation of mathematics in the same period.

Music

It is well known that mathematicians are often lovers of music but some are deaf to its beauty. One might wonder whether there is a parallel between this difference and the well-established difference between analysts and geometers—more precisely, between mathematicians who are chiefly interested in abstract structures and those who prefer to study models. But this is not the approach we wish to pursue; nor the study of the physical bases of music, which utilizes the mathematical tool of integers and fractions. What interests us most is the evolution of musical structure and the conscious grasp of it by the composer, for it is almost completely parallel to the evolution of mathematics.

For centuries people made music as they made mathematics —from a need that was instinctive, intuitive, esthetic, mystic, religious. Then people began to write about music as they wrote about mathematics; see the treatises on music by Aristoxenus (350 B.C.) who wished to give priority to feeling as opposed to the

"harmony by computation" of the Pythagoreans, and by Euclid *
and later Boethius (500 A.D.) whose essay was copied throughout
the Middle Ages and printed at the end of the fifteenth century
with his arithmetic and his geometry. In the eleventh century, at
the time of the appearance in the West of the number notation
which the Arabs had got from the Indies, Guy D'Arezzo gave his
name to the musical notation by placing notes on a staff.

Up to the eighteenth century, manuals and textbooks on music
were common, music being considered a branch of mathematics.
What was the quality of the instruction? According to Jacques
Chailley, "in the sixteenth century music pupils were taught the
structure of the Greek chromatic scale, which had already become
outdated in the time of Sophocles." (The lag in science teaching
existed before our day!) And Chailley adds that in a harmony
treatise still in use, the indicated classification of consonances had
lost its reason for existence in the first third of the fourteenth
century, not to mention the annoying circumstance that the word
media ("intermediate") was translated as "mixed." We seem to
hear an echo of the warning given recently by the Bourbakist Jean
Dieudonné: "At the present moment the mathematics taught in our
schools corresponds approximately to what was known in 1640."

The research of present-day musicologists, particularly that of
Chailley, helps us to understand how melodic structures have
evolved from primitive music (as it still exists among some peoples
out of the path of our civilization) to classical music. At first, one
fundamental note and the first overtones are used alone; outside
the relation of equivalence which is the octave, the fifth and the
fourth are known. Then the third appears, which introduces a new
harmonic structure, that of the perfect chord. Then combinations
of structures may emerge. Musicians of the late nineteenth century,
particularly Ravel, introduced echoes of the primitive structure
into their works, giving them a certain color. Shall we call them
comparable to Gaspard Monge, the eighteenth-century mathema-

* Actually "Euclid's" book on music was written by Cleonides, and
Eudoxus did the sixth book of the *Elements*. It seems likely that the biog-
raphy of Euclid is very similar to that of "Bourbaki"!

tician who treated questions of metric geometry by means of projective geometry and thus combined Euclid with the seventeenth-century's Gerard Desargues?

But these innovations were introduced by the intuition of genius. A period of excessive axiomatization later arrived, bringing about finally, along with the knowledge and understanding of the elementary structures, the possibility of creating new ones.

Let us quote Stuckenschmidt again: "The generation of composers around 1900 was no longer caught between the two fires of 'pure music' and 'musical drama.' The struggle it had to face was on a wholly different plane, and its critical scope was revealed as more considerable: at stake was the reconsideration of the validity of the musical material itself. The outlines of crisis became clear at the beginning of the century, and this crisis led to a creative, dialectic resolution. It was the most grievous, the most important, the most consequential moment music had experienced since the birth of the classic style in the seventeenth century and perhaps since the advent of monodic music about 1600. Actually for the first time in its existence, music brought into question the rational principles on which it was based. Every important work of the twentieth century is based on the rejection of those traditional laws of harmony which the chords of Tristan had already destroyed."

Upon what concepts are the strict laws of the seventeenth and eighteenth centuries founded, and what guarantees their validity, or even more, their necessity? Have not all of them been transgressed, more or less, by all the great composers? But such transgressions were probably occasional, exceptional, in order precisely to give the audience an unaccustomed effect, to express a feeling of disquiet or of terror, to evoke fantastic or supernatural visions. In the twentieth century we face not exceptions to the rule but a change of the rule itself. Why only major and minor tonalities? Does not the mathematician work, if he wishes, in a non-Euclidean space? Why the predominance of a tonic? The mind has accustomed itself to the relativity of the vertical; cannot the ear accept a scale of twelve sounds put on a footing of equality? After fifteen years of trials and discussions, Schoenberg, Stravinsky, and many others made new codes, new norms. About 1915, Mathias Hauer chose a passage of several notes taken from the twelve sounds of the chromatic scale and explored the structures obtained by juxtaposing and combining all the intervals presented by that passage —a simple exercise in calculation from which every emotional element is excluded. This leads us, of course, to exercises for a calculating machine! Actually, some music was written expressly for mechanical pianos, then for magnetic tape which the composer manipulated in the recording studio, for fear that a performer might introduce some human element in interpreting it.

The non-specialist listener, facing such a construction, can only react as a technician would before a page of symbolic logic or advanced modern mathematics; he finds himself before an incomprehensible black magic. Even if it is explained, even if he is given the key, it is a matter without interest. The contradiction between order conceived and order perceived—is it not parallel to the divergence between theory contemplated and theory formalized? Nevertheless the comparison itself shows that a non-musician must be prudent about criticism, for a condemnation made simply on the basis of what we like or on the basis of rules previously accepted has scarcely any value; if we do not understand, the only reasonable attitude is to stay away from the concert or not to look at the manuscript. Fortunately there are other criteria: first, the honest approval of a fairly large and sincere group of men working in the same direction may indicate that our judgment is not competent and should be reserved; and then there is the test of time. Let us not speak of the twelve-tone school of music and of whether its rigor has softened. For mathematics, the test of time has been up to this moment triumphantly surmounted.

But there is another criterion, and here the parallel stops. The serious point is that the new law, in music, forbade all use of the old harmony, rejected every perfect chord, every fifth, every fourth, everything that had traditionally been considered harmonic; instead of a liberation, of an enlargement of the artist's possibilities, of a multiplication of possible structures, it became a matter of despotism. Even if the new law does permit a rich and varied work (which will have to be proved) in what way is it better than the old? But this is not the situation in modern mathematics. Lobachevsky did not forbid the geometry of Euclid, any more than Einstein made Newton seem outdated and unfashionable. Mathematics in our day is after all nothing but a game—each person is free to choose the rules and to consecrate his life to it at his own risk—but a scientific game is permitted to integrate itself into science only on certain conditions which must be precisely stated. These conditions will appear when we show the characteristics of modern mathematics, although the conditions are perhaps neither obvious nor permanent. In any case, the progress of civilization in general requires us to enrich its possibilities and not to restrict them; to complete, not to mutilate; to reject only that which is contradictory to the whole or dangerous to civilization itself. Whatever the law which each imposes upon himself, and whatever the road which he thinks will lead to progress, that is to say, whatever his "rules of the game," the doctrine, even in art, ought to be liberal. One can join in what Busoni, an avant-garde theoretician and music teacher, wrote around 1920: "I know only one thing worse than trying to oppose progress, and that is throwing oneself into it head down. . . . One must sift and exploit all the victories assured by the experiences of the past in order to build them into rigorous and beautiful forms."

Painting

The study of the modern movement in painting might seem to take us very far from our subject. It would be artificial to seek a systematic parallel between this art and mathematics. The painter, by the very nature of his work, is drawn in different directions between, on the one hand, his vision of the external world, his dream, his sensibility, his abstract intelligence, critical and at the same time creative, his powers of analysis and of synthesis, the mass of elements he must control, and, on the other hand, his tools, his flat, blank canvas, his pencil and his charcoal, his tubes of colors (for

in our day he no longer prepares colors himself). He is forced to
undertake the struggle which makes the greatness of his mission;
his weapon is the technique he has acquired by study. Will he know
what he owes to himself or to his school? To tradition? And what
will he wish to attain? The universal and the permanent? Or the
fleeting expression of a sensation? Does he wish to bring a condition or an idea to expression for himself, or does he wish to communicate it to others and be understood by them? All these attitudes are conceivable, and since all were actually adopted by one
artist or another at the beginning of the century, nothing has been
more varied and more individual than the paintings in which all
these tendencies appear. They do indeed group themselves into
schools, but remain mixed, fluid and unfixed, like the clouds floating
in the sky.

It is from physics rather than from mathematics that we bor-
row comparisons with painting, and from poetry or philosophy.
Painting is too much colored by dreams, too charged with the sub-
conscious, to develop or reject or transpose: the artist seeks equiva-
lents by suggestion; but his symbols will be polyvalent in spite
of himself, depending on who receives his message. The mathematician, on the contrary, uses symbols polyvalent by explicit definition; they are useful for the expression of theories from which all
trace of the sensibility of man has disappeared. (Some painters, of
course, have tried even that!)

At the turn of the century the rapidity of the evolution of the
sciences, the abundance of new facts that challenged every theory
of physics, the revolution in conceptions of nature, of energy, of
life, and at the same time a dizzying evolution of social conditions
—all this truly led the artist to question everything afresh. Perhaps the mathematician was the only privileged person; in his abstract speculations he was positive that reason would triumph.
Despite all discussions on the bases of science (which, like all his
fellow human beings, he had to revise), drawn like the rest into
discussions with no visible outcome, he appeared to be the least
disabled. As Lebesgue remarked in 1938: "At the moment when
Cantor seemed to call arithmetic into question, no one was upset.

Similarly in the historic epoch of the paradoxes on the theory of sets, after a discussion in which not one of us had shown a way to weld anew a logic which seemed forever broken, once back home we nevertheless continued to apply that same logic to the question we were studying; for an attitude of philosophic doubt taken in the course of a discussion in no way prevents complete certainty. Logic was incapable of shaking the absolute faith we had in applied logic! But we all know how easy it is to apply it wrongly."

What a contrast between the calm of the great mathematician and the terror revealed by a historian of painting of the same period! Here is René Huyghe's description in *The Contemporaries:* "Science knows that it is necessary to check everything at its base, to admit nothing as true unless one has clearly seen it so; in a word, to start with a clean slate. . . . The very foundations of Western culture were to be reconsidered. The twentieth century intends to rebuild only on complete and fierce certainties, at any cost. . . . It sanctions the downfall of the ideas that served as the basis of European civilization—the idea of the real, and the idea of reason. . . . Solid matter, that positive substance identified with the real—now it doesn't exist any more. . . . Intelligence has come up against the limit of its possibilities; it moves in these new zones only with the approval of mathematics."

After the last leap of realism which, with the Impressionists, pushed the passionate quest of reality so far that, according to the critic Bernard Dorival, they "ended in the creation of a world very foreign to reality," the Nabis sought to use lines and colors to translate their abstract conception of art, to suggest an impression rather than to copy nature. Then came the Fauves and Cubists: their efforts arouse the interest of the mathematician. They refused to represent space on the plane of the picture by means of perspective, considering this an outworn convention. They worked in two-dimensional space (for the Fauves, objects are colored spots without depth) or perhaps in an abstract space where planes were juxtaposed according to the whim of the artist. The Cubist studied forms; any cross section could be useful. He even worked in time-space!

We shall go no farther in this review of contradictory efforts to create a doctrine to reconcile the most divergent demands; we shall not wonder, with the surrealists, whether "the process of consciousness is no longer to be carried out, if the intelligence need not be taken into account; the dream alone can be applied for the solution of the fundamental questions of life." We leave the artist to his vocation of creating beauty despite his ignorance, his doubts, his anguish—or perhaps because of them. We leave the analogies which are perhaps synchronisms or perhaps influences: Debussy and Impressionism, Proust and Bergson, Gide and Fauvism; or, as Dorival suggests, Rouault and Claudel, Matisse and Valery, Dufy and Giraudoux.

All this effervescence is the mark of a contemporary movement too deep for any thinker to be able to remain completely aloof. The scientist who knows how a science is made is less troubled by his own creation than the layman who sees in this conception the collapse of the naive ones in which he had faith; but the scientist understands his present task: to rebuild an edifice, tentatively sufficient, which will be modern science.

The Natural Sciences

In looking at what has happened in science, let us restrict ourselves to recalling the changes in our conception of the physical universe since the beginning of this century. Similar observations might be made in the biological sciences.

The difference between mathematical science and physical science has never been very clear. There are evidently two extreme tendencies corresponding to opposed mental attitudes—on the one hand, the urge to accumulate observations; on the other, to construct theories logically scaffolded. But already the classification of the results of observation and, *a fortiori*, experimentation supposes an abstract theory which can have only a structure more or less mathematical and which moreover uses mathematics as a tool. Conversely, much of the mathematics of all epochs fears the mark of the structure imposed by the physical model that gave it birth: for example, whatever may be the present concept of fractions, it is clear that their origin, the measurement of size, still guides our intuition. I may concern myself very little with my friend's great-grandfather and yet not deny that the ancestor imposed several character traits on his present descendant, and this is even clearer if I compare my friend with his still-living father. The measurement of size is a living chapter of physics—it is mensuration.

Shall we say that the sciences of physics and mathematics differ in their aims? In 1894 Paul Tannery wrote: "Geometry has for its aim the study of the size and the form of material objects, abstractions made from their essence." But the proposed definition scarcely fits present-day mathematics. We shall certainly have to pose the question of the relations between mathematics and the real world when we try to characterize the first. As far as physics is concerned, its object seems clear enough, at least for the non-specialist. Like Molière's philosophy teacher, we might say: "Physics is that which explains the principles of natural things and the properties of bodies; which discusses the nature of elements, of metals, of minerals, of stones, of plants, and of animals; and which teaches us the causes of meteors, rainbows, shooting-stars, comets, lightning, thunder, rain, snow, hail, winds and cyclones." We know the reaction of Jourdain. There is certainly plenty of chaos to elucidate! Pretensions in former times were modest, however, and explanations simple: If some Jupiter hurled a thunderbolt, one did not insist too much on knowing the physical nature of lightning.

It is well known how the invention of instruments of observation and measurement, by continuously discovering new aspects of reality, gave rise to various theories of physics, and how, in turn, the theories permitted the invention of new instruments. Even more, the very method of physics leads often to "the conversion of an object of study into an instrument of research." A classic example is the case of alpha particles related by J. Robert Oppenheimer in *Science and the Common Understanding*.

One of the essential stages in the evolution of physics was certainly the invention of precise instruments for the measurement of time. (Christian Huygens's treatise on the regulation of clocks dates from 1673.) We can hardly imagine life in a society with only a vague notion of time, or a physics without time playing a quantitative role. Chronometry raised kinetics to the rank of a science, and it then became a branch of mathematics. Paraphrasing Tannery, we might say that kinetics studies the variations in time of the forms and the relative positions of material objects. "Kinetics is then in abstraction made of the causes of these movements," the cause itself being in the domain of physics.

But almost immediately science, by its very nature as an enterprise of mental activity based on observations of the senses, separates itself from the real even while feeding on it, as a great tree holds to the ground only by its roots. Kinetics and dynamics speak of objects that fall, of springs deformed, of threads pulled taut; but they have also had to create new objects, abstract and freely conceived, which little by little have imposed themselves: force, mass, acceleration, quantity of movement, centrifugal and centripetal force. While still a young student at the Lycée, I wondered anxiously: is it $\frac{1}{2} mv^2$ or mv^2 that is really in the phenomenon studied? I did not know that science creates the objects of its study at the same time it creates the method that permits the study, and that these objects do not exist in external reality but exist only because the thinking of the physicist has created them. As soon as these conceptual objects are abstracted from perceived objects, physics becomes "mathematicized"; at his own risk the scientist formulates laws from which the theory will be elaborated. Confidence will come if the confrontation of the predictions and the experimental verifications show no serious disagreements; otherwise it will be necessary either to abandon the conceived entities as monsters incapable of life, or of subjecting them to other laws. Out of the love of his creation the scientist will try to take the second choice, giving the name "corrections" to the changes he must make. The fact is that the physicist readily attributes a concrete reality, independent of the human spirit, to the objects he handles so familiarly in his theories; we shall find again this psychological phenomenon of the displacement of what is felt as "concrete" when we examine the evolution of mathematics.

The mechanist believed in the reality of the little pellets which, subjected to the laws of mechanics, apparently constituted matter; he sought in the visible a representation and a manifestation of the invisible: the Brownian movement was simultaneously an enlarged image of molecular agitation and an intermediary for studying it. "A time will come perhaps when atoms, finally seen directly, will be as easy to observe as microbes are today," wrote Jean Perrin in 1913.

Nevertheless the phenomena of light, electricity and heat led physicists in another direction; they introduced other concepts: rays, waves, speeds of propagation. . . . We still find "energy" there, but in quite a different form, in spite of an "equivalence" in the mechanical energy. The favorite, familiar, indispensable concept of the energy proponents was the ether, the fluid whose vibrations produced light. For Gabriel Lamé in the mid-nineteenth century the existence of the ether was "incontestably proved," and for Lord Kelvin, "ether is not an imaginary creation of the speculative philosopher; it is as necessary to us as the air we breathe; the study of this substance which permeates all is perhaps the most fascinating task and the most important one in all of physics."

Despite all this, the only real object of knowledge for the mechanist was the geometric aspect that locates the object in space and the date that locates it in time. The variations (with respect to time) of geometric magnitudes (distances, angles) made possible a description of phenomena by the laws of dynamics, and a preview of its evolution. Such was the character of the nineteenth-century mechanist's determinism. For the proponents of energy the object of knowledge was the field where waves are propagated, the components of the vectors that represented the electrical and magnetic states of ether. Couldn't one attempt to reconcile these two points of view, or to extend each until it could become the domain of application of the other?

Such seemed the task to be accomplished toward the end of the last century. Fourier, for example, had succeeded in putting into remarkable mathematical form the energy theory of heat: could not a form of the dynamic theory be found which would be equivalent and which would differ from it only in interpretation, in the choice of the model? Despite the persistent duality of matter-energy and some still inexplicable phenomena such as gravity, the success of physics was brilliant. It had really become a major science, a classical science, and with the help of mathematics, which had finally mastered its own rigorous methods, there was hope of constructing a chart of the universe, descriptive and explanatory, becoming more and more adequate yet simultaneously simpler, more harmonious, achieving beauty with unity.

It was at this point that a review of values unexpectedly became necessary in physics as it had in the other fields of human activities. The atom was becoming more and more prodigiously empty, and Jean Perrin, whom we quoted above, leaned dizzily over "matter, indefinitely discontinuous, piercing a continuous ether with miniscule stars." At the same time astronomy, too, gave us vertigo with the newly discovered immensity of the universe. The first stellar distances had been measured in 1840, and had not greatly upset man's conception of the universe; but the spiral form of the nebulae, noted around 1850 and confirmed in 1887 by the great nebula of Andromeda, finally revealed its secret: there were now other universes analogous to the one that had seemed the All. Then the chart of the arrangement of matter, or what was left of it, had to be done again (any last doubts were to be removed in 1925). Energy, at least, remained for a time a domain in which the continuous triumphed with the electromagnetic theory of Maxwell, who interpreted the waves of Fresnel. "But," recalls Louis de Broglie, "an unexpected event occurred in theoretical physics. The problem of 'black radiation' preoccupied physicists at that time. To emerge from the difficult situation, Max Planck in 1900 tried a heroic remedy; he introduced an entirely new element, completely unknown to classical physics: 'the quantum of action.' But this brilliant success had disquieting aspects."

Emile Picard wrote in 1933: "The constant of Planck limits

our knowledge of nature." Einstein, toward the end of his life, told de Broglie, "I must resemble an ostrich which constantly buries its head in relativist sand in order not to have to face these ugly quanta." (Does this not recall Hermite, unable to bear the thought of functions without derivatives, which he had helped to introduce?) But it was Einstein himself who had given the quanta clear citizenship rights in 1905! As de Broglie puts it: "During this crucial year in the history of physics, by a double master-stroke of which there probably exists no other example in the history of science, Albert Einstein introduced one after the other two fundamental ideas in the theory of physics which were going to change completely the course of its evolution: the idea of the relativity of space and time and the idea of the quanta of light."

The special theory of relativity took a firm grip on the mind as soon as it was presented (*e.g.*, when Paul Langevin introduced it in 1922 to the literary students at Sèvres). Since simultaneity is not defined for events which do not coincide in space, one must consider different times suitable to different systems in movement with respect to each other. The general theory of relativity somehow seems less convincing. Does it really sentence us to live in "Einstein's mollusk," where only topological relations remain, and in comparison with which the spaces of Lobachevsky or of Riemann seem paradises? In any case, one agrees with de Broglie that "the pleasant little article [of 1905] was like a thunderclap in an almost clear sky and the crisis it started has not ended even now, half a century later."

We need not debate here the two divergent currents that sprang from the unexpected source which had just gushed forth. Must we accept a probabilistic view of the universe, renouncing precise descriptions in time and space, abandoning causality and determinism in physical phenomena, adopting Heisenberg's principle of uncertainty, Bohr's complementarity and Pauli's principle of exclusion? Or can we perhaps hope that de Broglie's theory of wave mechanics and his method of the double solution will triumph over the purely probabilistic interpretation which Einstein rejected? In our incompetence, we can only admire all these attempts and the spectacular success they attain in their explanations of the phenomena of nature—for example, in throwing light on the composition of metals or on the state of matter in the white dwarfs, those strange stars discovered in 1910, in which the density of matter is of the order of one ton per cubic centimeter. All the work of present-day physicists is now interpreted in the light of the modern theories, whether in the field of optics, electricity, thermodynamics or, naturally, electronics.

From the point of view that interests us here, we may well be amazed to note that the theorist in physics finds at his disposal all the usable tools of mathematics. But mathematics did not remain frozen in an outdated tradition either. Sometimes mathematics ran ahead of the needs of the physicists. One often hears the example of conic sections studied by the Greeks for their pure beauty, which furnished Kepler with the elliptical model suited to the trajectory of planets. But many other examples might be given: thus Lobachevsky, in constructing his "Pangeometry," could not foresee that relativity would use this model of space to account for the structure of the universe; similarly, when Hermite imagined the quadratic forms that bear his name (Hermitian forms) for arithmetic considerations, no one could have dreamed that they would be used almost a century later for the modern theory of quanta. Sometimes, on the other hand, the physicists gave leads to the mathematicians. Fourier's theory of heat is a famous example; it was destined to renovate the notion of function and of the development of functions in series. In the same way, it was for the needs of physics and with their techniques that mathematicians first attacked the problem Dirichlet posed of finding whether the values taken by a function on the boundary of a region permit the determination of the values of this function in an interior point of the region, and this led to the refinement of the notion of harmonic function and to a study of discontinuities. Of the results, Picard wrote in 1893: "The demonstration given by Riemann is presented with insufficient rigor, but at least it makes very probable the theorem in question and it is of the type of reasoning frequently employed in mathematical physics, with which, for lack of something better, one must often be satisfied." Give way to the mathematicians! Picard cites New-mann, Schwarz, Poincaré; to make exact the conditions of the theorem, these men studied the various cases of discontinuities of certain kinds, for sets of certain types, and on surfaces which no longer had anything but a slight resemblance to those of elementary geometry.

This example alone shows clearly the tendencies that impose themselves on modern mathematics, even if, and perhaps especially if, they wish to be of use to physics: the need for rigor; the study of sets; generalizations of naive notions such as those of curve or surface or, above all, the notion of function in which continuity appears as a convenient though special case; the study of equations of various types which, by considerable effort, are reduced to forms accessible to theoretical study and effective calculation.

To overcome difficulties in the theories of particles, even in their early forms, work was produced in another direction, that of statistics and the calculation of probabilities. (Pascal, who helped formulate the theory of probability in the seventeenth century, would not have been surprised to see it taking on great importance in the social sciences, but he certainly did not dream of any need for it in the science of matter.) Several methods of making statistics and probability useful to the particle theories were suggested by Borel: he proposed replacing the infinite with a large number which would permit the introduction of averages, replacing a very large number of functions of one variable by one function of two variables of which one is a parameter of the primitive theory, or even introducing an infinite number of functions of an infinite number of variables in spaces with an infinite number of dimensions. And how many other areas of mathematics were to experience such an unforeseeable expansion!

To conclude on the subject of physics, let us admire the eager and ever-growing crowd of initiates who unite in a prodigious collective labor. Instead of sharing the confusion of those who, unable to conceive more than the simple and the obvious, belittle human intelligence because it cannot explain everything by some great magic Word, let us listen to the dignified and optimistic affirmation of the mathematician, the clear resolve of the physicist, the enthusiasm of the astronomer:

Emile Picard, the mathematician:

"We no longer pretend to be able to grasp reality in a physical theory; we see in it rather an analytic or geometric mold useful and fertile for a tentative representation of phenomena, no longer believing that the agreement of a theory with experience demonstrates that the theory expresses the reality of things. Such statements have sometimes seemed discouraging; we ought rather to marvel that, with representations of things more or less distant and discolored, the human spirit has been able to find its way through the chaos of so many phenomena and to derive from scientific knowledge the ideas of beauty and harmony. It is no paradox to say that science puts order, at least tentative order, into nature."

J. Robert Oppenheimer, the physicist:

"Time and experience have clarified, refined and enriched our understanding of these notions. Physics has changed since then. It will change even more. But what we have learned so far, we have learned well. If it is radical and unfamiliar and a lesson that we are not likely to forget, we think that the future will be only more radical and not less, only more strange and not more familiar, and that it will have its own new insights for the inquiring human spirit."

Paul Couderc, the astronomer:

"The only conceptions that succumb are those that pretend to fix the image of a profound reality: true relations among things survive, united to the true new relations in the burgeoning theory. Let us then rejoice at the massacre of old theories because this is the criterion of progress. There is, I think, no ground for fear that nature will undernourish the seekers. Nothing should diminish our enthusiasm for the experimental victories, decisive and definitive, of the past thirty years."

III

For twenty-five centuries mathematicians have been in the habit of correcting their errors—and seeing their science enriched rather than impoverished thereby. This gives them the right to contemplate the future with serenity.

—NICOLAS BOURBAKI

THE NEW TRENDS
IN MATHEMATICS

We have just reviewed the twentieth-century revision of the values that had been inherited from three centuries of classical thinking in the arts and natural sciences. This revolution inevitably penetrated into mathematics, because while mathematics, as a science of abstract and eternal verities, claims to dominate the struggle, it still recognizes its mission as an instrument for knowledge of the real world and its responsibility for building structures whereby this knowledge can be organized into theories. But more than that, at the very time of the revolution in the natural sciences, mathematics found itself compelled to re-examine its own traditional values. To the needs of physics, mathematics responded efficiently by its own power of expansion, using all its resources to create new concepts and to utilize these concepts immediately as tools, as physicists have done in more concrete forms. However, this work of reconstruction on the edifice was undermining the underlying foundation that had been erected by the philosophy of Plato, the science of Euclid, and the logic of Aristotle.

Modern mathematics appeared on the scene with two compulsions. On the one hand, it wished to adventure in all directions, fearlessly, even rashly, to go ahead preparing the areas in which the researcher could specialize to meet the needs of physics or of his own curiosity. On the other hand, mathematics intended to reconstruct the supports of the edifice to ensure a broader foundation, conceived extensively enough to support all that the near future might bring, insofar as that could actually be anticipated, and, if one had sufficient courage, to erect a new structure within which all theories would find their place. Finally, metamathematics, from the sidelines, supervised the laying of the structure and even arrogated to itself the right of passing judgment on the solidity of the whole. We shall indicate in the next few chapters the grand outline of this construction. Here we wish merely to recall quickly the principal currents of history that have brought us to the present state, for we cannot understand the spirit of modern mathematics if we consider it as merely the gratuitous fantasies of novelty-seekers. Justification by continuity is at least as important as justification by intrinsic beauty or by utility. Moreover, all treatises that expound fundamental theories today contain historic overviews which assert that, in spite of novelties, they do not renounce the past. We can do no better than refer the reader to the remarkable "Historic Notes" of the various books of the *Elements of Mathematics* of Nicolas Bourbaki, which highlight the evolution of ideas, of the origins of the present state of affairs. (See also, with reference to algebra, the "Commentaries" in the two volumes of A. Chatelet's *Modern Arithmetic and Algebra,* 1954–1957.)

The continuity of mathematics has often been threatened but always retained, from the era of the civilizations of Egypt and Babylon to our own day. It is this continuity that we must keep in mind if we wish to see the contemporary movement in its proper perspective.

Mathematics is the science of numbers, which our experience with solid bodies imposes on our minds, and the science of space, in which these bodies exist and can move without our losing the knack of recognizing them, thanks to our memories and our powers of abstraction. Such could have been the definition of primitive mathematics, though it was even then twofold in its aims and its methods. Must we therefore say: "Arithmetic was developed to permit scribes to collect taxes and make inventories of goods; geometry was invented to measure and distribute the deposits left at each overflowing of the sacred Nile, which each year gave a gift of fertile soil to the Pharaoh's people"? It is very probable that to this utilitarian and technical aspect (which, as the example of China proves, is sufficient to permit the construction of instruments and a primitive architecture) there corresponded already a theoretical science, bordering on magic and surrounded by mysticism, which has not revealed its secret to us, and which the priest-scribes of the Houses of Life transmitted to one another by word of mouth. Just so did the god Thot himself dictate his revelations to his disciple Nebmertouf, shown crouched before his master in the two small monuments preserved at the Louvre.

Hieroglyphic writing has symbols for the causal relations which we translate by: *therefore, if—then, because, although, in order that, even if,* etc. A logic so explicitly written indicates thinking that has risen considerably above empirical knowledge. The preliminary traces left on incompleted bas-reliefs indicate a geometry which may have been magical, probably mystical, but which was certainly abstract and not vulgarly utilitarian, imposing its own rules and setting itself above the observation of the real.

As for arithmetic, the work of Bruin on the Rhind papyrus of Egypt indicates the existence of a technique of integers and unit-fractions (fractions with numerator one) which presupposes a detailed and powerful knowledge of the first few hundred integers. Mathematics has already begun, since on the models imposed by reality there is superimposed an abstract conception of permanent entities susceptible of many representations, always resembling themselves despite the transformations that their appearance undergoes through space and in the course of time.

But the human mind attributes a reality to the object it creates. The displacement of the "concrete," which we have already met in physics, is apparent at this stage of mathematics. In any case, these already familiar elements (the straight line and its segments, the plane, the circle, the sphere and the intersections of these figures, as well as the regions they determine) were endowed by Plato's philosophy with an absolute existence which the human mind learned by revelation and which assured the validity of geometry. In addition, the atomic conception of matter and space established what might be called the geometry of the theorem of Thales: two segments, since they are formed of atoms, always have a common aliquot part, a multiple of the size of the atom, so that the fractions are perfectly adequate to their task of measuring size; parallels joining two atoms of two secants determine segments containing whole numbers of atoms, numbers which are obviously proportional (whence the notion of proportional segments). Such were the implicit foundations of the mathematics codified by Euclid, using the logic expounded and organized by Aristotle as an autonomous science. The mathematical problem seemed therefore completely defined, and it had a character of absolute certitude.

But immediately difficulties appeared because of the need for introducing the infinite. What could be simpler than to consider a square, to trace the circle of which the center is one of the vertices and which passes through the opposite vertex? Does this circle cut the sides of the square that begin at the center, if they are extended? If not, everything we have assumed about the existence of intersections and the properties of order must be rejected, and the whole of geometry is destroyed.

But if the answer is yes, the ratio x of the radius of the circle to the length of the side must have as its square the integer 2. Now the square root of 2 does not exist as a rational number, and the geometry of the theorem of Thales is destroyed. That is the antinomy which cannot be avoided; that is the scandal of the irrationals. Naturally, we will face it at every turn, for once mathematical research is detached from the real, it has no limits except its desire for coherence and its aspiration for harmony, for unity, which is often subjected to acid tests. It was not for a practical end that the problem of the duplication of the cube was attacked so vigorously, despite the situation to which legend attributes its origin. The demand for its solution by the Delphic oracle in return for putting an end to a certain epidemic was no more compelling than that the fall of an apple should require relating gravity on earth to the revolution of the moon in the sky. And the "passing to the limit" of Archimedes was concerned with interests quite different from providing good formulas for wine and oil merchants in the gauging of their urns!

It is well known how Eudoxus met the difficulty of the irrationals by isolating them, approaching them and bracketing them by means of fractions, with a theory so nice that for us it constitutes a veritable modern definition. To his mind there was no such thing as the irrational number. Yet his stratagems were vain, and these irrationals, which cropped up everywhere, were used more or less openly during 20 centuries, as if they really existed, as if they were really numbers. The history of numbers is full of these recurring scandals: roots which are fictitious, absurd, false, negative— whatever you wish to call them—they are certainly not numbers! Neither are imaginary roots, but one grows accustomed to using them like numbers! The great Larousse dictionary said in 1873: "Imaginaries in mathematics are a form of the impossible. Algebra up to now has furnished only two forms of the impossible: the negative and the imaginary." But what is this algebra which, upon meeting the impossible, does not halt, but uses it as though existence were attributed to the elements whose existence is denied?

One of the triumphs of the nineteenth century was the solution of this difficulty by the introduction into mathematics of a new entity, still called "number" although hardly resembling any longer the natural whole number or the fraction. It was obtained in two ways. First, by an extension creating a set which is more abundant in elements and in which the sets previously known form only one subset. For example, the fraction, a set of two integers, takes on the aspect of a rational number in which the whole number is a particular case. Numbers formed with the help of radicals (irrational numbers) constitute a still richer set; this set is included in the set of algebraic numbers (roots of equations obtained by setting equal to zero a polynomial with rational coefficients) ; and the set of algebraic numbers, in turn, is included in a still richer set. Liouville in 1844 gave examples of non-algebraic numbers; Hermite in 1873 and Lindemann in 1882 proved respectively that numbers already introduced under the symbols π and e are not algebraic. Such numbers are called *transcendental*. But what are their properties? Should we classify these, too, in various categories which are more and more general? The question seems to be preliminary to algebra, in the sense that algebra operates on these numbers, and one should know what they are. This was one of the roads that led to the study of the theory of sets established by Georg Cantor in 1874.

The second procedure for introducing new numbers was to recognize various structures that distinguish the known sets; for example, the name "number" has been given to complex numbers although a natural order is not attributed to them, yet that property is nevertheless the most fundamental in the number-measure of size! (If we define a complex number as smaller than another when its modulus is the smaller of the two, some numbers will at times be neither smaller nor larger than others unless they are equal to them!) If we accept not only non-ordering but also non-commutativity of multiplication, we can create new "numbers" such as quaternions (Hamilton, 1863) or other hyper-complex numbers. The analysis of the diverse structures of the number-measures, and the creation of new numbers by a choice of the structures which one wished to preserve—this is the method of *axiomatic creation*. These two procedures were not to be followed without some miscalculations!

The mathematician's "space" also has changed considerably in the course of the centuries. After Descartes it became arithmetized: the plane became the set of ordered pairs of numbers; space, the set of the ordered tercets (if one may apply this word to numbers as well as to verses). But why stop there? Why not consider $4, 5, \cdots n$ "dimensions"? To go back, the straight line itself will no longer be a complete entity handed down as a sort of revelation from a superior existence; it will be a set of numbers (or, if one prefers, a set of points of which the numbers are the measures). But what numbers? The numbers of measurement? The negative numbers? We realize how abstract the notion of number has become when we follow the efforts of geometers to find a concrete representation for them. It now seems incredible that it should have been only Lazare Carnot, and then Michel Chasles, who made the negative number appear in geometry and who thus created an abstract space of which the figures of diverse dispositions are only representations. (Let us note that in Chasles' voluminous and meticulous work there is no suggestion of the possibility of also introducing a convention of signs for angles. Was it lack of imagination, or an awareness of the difficulties that such an attempt would encounter—difficulties which were surmounted only by use of Gauss's arithmetic congruences?)

The interpretation of imaginary numbers required more imagination because they are not ordered: they cannot be used for measuring and appear to be "complexes." Around 1800 Wessel and then Argand gave these complexes a geometric reality by interpreting them by translations and rotations in the plane. (This is what Hamilton sought to generalize with his quarternions.) One can then attribute to the complexes a trigonometric form, and they are represented by a vector or by a point on a plane: the complex plane. But now every point of the plane is the image of just *one* number! What would Descartes say about that? Is the complex plane, then, a straight line? Where will it lead us if we give the name *curve* to the locus of the points whose coordinates are x and y, which in turn are bound by an equation $f(x, y) = 0$? It is instructive to consider for a moment the reply to this question, presented around 1842 as the only possible reply, by an enemy of Cauchy's—Maximilien Marie. He associated to the couple (x, y) when the numbers are imaginaries $x = x' + ix''$, $y = y' + iy''$, the point with coordinates $X = x' + y'$, $Y = x'' + y''$, remarking that this correspondence continues after a change of rectangular coordinates. But the relation $f(x, y) = 0$ that defines the curve, with the two relations of definition of X and Y, gives only four equalities, and this does not permit the elimination of x', x'', y', y''. Nevertheless we want to obtain a "curve"—that is, a relation of the type $F(X, Y) = 0$. To attain this end, Marie decided to impose the condition $y'' = C y'$, C being a constant chosen to simplify the representation. Each value of C gives a curve "conjugate" to the given curve. (Thus the conjugate of the circle $x^2 + y^2 = R^2$ relative to $C = 0$ is the hyperbola $X^2 - Y^2 = R^2$.) And the author utilized this representation to treat certain problems of algebra and even of analysis. Today we consider this only a simple exercise and not an element in the architecture of mathematics. Why? Because, if an interpretation is to be accepted as the *model* of an abstract theory, it must preserve all its structures; the structures needed for the representation, which are necessarily added afterwards, must be recognized and yet not remain in the conclusions. As far as the imaginaries are concerned, we know that $f(x, y) = 0$ can be interpreted as a correspondence between the points of two complex planes. But what happens to the idea of curve?

Let us return to the space of the geometers, where number is not the primordial element. Toward the end of the fifteenth century painters and sculptors systematized the procedures that had been used more or less consciously up to their time to make a correspondence between the points of spaces of two and of three dimensions. Leonardo da Vinci and Albrecht Dürer in particular created perspective and even descriptive geometry (which Monge was to construct three centuries later) to represent three-dimensional space on a two-dimensional plane; the art of bas-relief led to a correspondence between the three-dimensional space of the model and another three-dimensional space, by the transformation which we now call affinity. In the seventeenth century Desargues transferred these transformations to the plane, creating homology. In the nineteenth century Monge, Poncelet and Chasles derived from all this the concept of projective space, where the distance between two points is no longer defined, and where the fundamental numerical element is the anharmonic ratio of four collinear points. It is the geometry of the ruler and compass as against the geometry of the ruler. Space therefore appears as structured *by the tools that are permissible,* which leads us again to the concept of an axiomatic creation.

At this time, moreover, the proof of the possibility of axiomatic creations was established, for Lobachevsky (1793–1856) had constructed his non-Euclidean geometry. The abstract non-Euclidean spaces, especially those introduced by Riemann, later became the ones in which relativity placed physical reality. But if conceptions of space can be made so abstract and built upon foundations so arbitrary, is there any limit to the possibilities of mathematical creation? And what is space?

By the eighteenth and nineteenth centuries number and space were no longer the only objects studied by mathematical science. The theory of algebraic equations was renewed by the introduction of *groups,* a notion which was created by Galois (1811–1832) in particular situations but which was to be one of the points of departure of a modern development in algebra. The *idea of function* penetrates algebra as well as geometry. Introduced by mechanics, function at first was considered simple enough to be studied in its complete generality. The notion of continuity was intuitive, and fortunately for the progress of mathematics, in the eyes of mathematicians in the time of Newton and Leibniz, all the functions had derivatives; it was difficult enough to attain an acceptable notion of it! To the differential calculus thus discovered was added the opposite construction of the integral calculus, and the work of Archimedes was belatedly rediscovered. At the same time, it was realized that these functions might be represented by entire series. Mechanics, even for Newton, led to considering functions as integrals of differential equations. The infinitesimal geometry of curves, extended to surfaces, demanded the introduction of equations with partial derivatives, necessary also for the mechanics of vibrating cords; but such a study of periodic phenomena led to the consideration of trigonometric series. Thus each forward step in mathematics engendered, by a chain of creation, the introduction of new entities which, as in physics, were used as tools for other studies and other creations.

The mathematician, perhaps even more than the physicist, never has the impression of a science completed and certain. Sometimes the current of discoveries rushes ahead at the expense of rigor, and contradictions appear; sometimes a great task of organization is undertaken but some new scandal arises at the very moment when the march forward has started confidently. The early nineteenth-century Norwegian mathematician Niels Abel described the state that mathematics was in when he entered it in these terms: "Divergent series are completely an invention of the devil, and it is a disgrace that any demonstration should be based on them. One can draw from them whatever one wishes when they are used—they are the ones that have produced so many failures and paradoxes. . . . Even the binomial theorem has not yet been rigorously demonstrated. . . . Taylor's theorem, the base of all higher mathematics, is just as poorly established. I have found only one rigorous demonstration of it—that of Cauchy." Actually, at the beginning of the nineteenth century Cauchy closed one period in the history of mathematics and inaugurated a new one which would appear to be less hazardous. He ruthlessly tested the product of three centuries, establishing an order and a rigor unknown before. He rejected as too vague the habitual appeals to "the generality of the analysis" and determined the conditions of validity of each formula depending on the functions introduced and the values attributed to the contained quantities: "In determining these conditions and these values and in fixing in a precise fashion the meaning of the notations I use, I cause all uncertainty to disappear." He did actually give rigorous definitions of continuity, of limits, of different sorts of convergences of sequences or series. With Cauchy himself setting the example, mathematics could start off again with a sure step!

But then, what happened during the second half of the century? A summary given by Emile Picard in a conference at Clark University in 1899 helps us to understand. In the light of the new demands of rigor, obeying the appeals of physics, mathematical notions appeared much more complex than was believed; generalizations changed the nature of the questions they propounded, and once again scandals appeared which again demanded a general remolding of the very conceptions of mathematics. Thus emerged modern mathematics.

The mathematician and physicist Boussinesq was astonished to learn in 1875 that there existed continuous functions without derivatives at any point. As Picard reports: "He said—very seriously, I think—that functions have everything to gain by having derivatives!" And still later, Hermite wrote to Stieltjès: "I turn away in fright and horror from this lamentable sore of functions which have no derivatives." Despite such general repugnance, and some desperate resistance, it became necessary to admit these monsters: Peano constructed a curve as the locus of a point whose coordinates are continuous functions of a parameter and which nevertheless passes through all the interior points of a square! Emile Picard in 1899 had to defend Henri Lebesgue when the Academy was on the point of rejecting his note describing the construction of surfaces which were applicable on the plane but which nevertheless were not the ruled and developable surfaces that classic theory had demonstrated to be the only ones applicable. Lebesgue commented in 1922: "Darboux in 1875 had devoted his *Mémoire* to integration and to functions without derivatives; he therefore did not experience the same horror as Hermite. Nevertheless I doubt whether he ever entirely forgave my *Note on Applicable Surfaces*. He must have thought that 'those who make themselves dull in this study are wasting their time instead of devoting it to useful research.'" On the contrary, Lebesgue adds, "I realized clearly from the beginning that such studies were useful, though I could not have said to what extent." In 1903 he wrote: "We may wonder if there is any point in occupying oneself with such complications, and whether it is not better to limit oneself to the study of functions that require only simple definitions. . . . But if one wished always to limit himself to the consideration of these well-behaved functions, it would be necessary to renounce the solution of many problems which were proposed long ago and in simple terms."

We might really see something arbitrary in these creations. They seemed to be particular cases, and monstrous ones at that, which one would not ordinarily encounter in the theories. Their value seemed to be merely in showing how necessary it was to be prudent in reasoning and to be suspicious of intuition. But it was not so; astonishing cases arose everywhere and demanded citizenship rights. Dirichlet specified the sufficient conditions for assuring the validity of the developments in series. Fourier had already bravely utilized systems of an infinite number of equations with an infinite number of unknowns; but it appeared, to DuBois-Reymond in particular, that a continuous function is not always necessarily developable in a trigonometric series. We quote again from Picard: "One quickly recognizes the need to establish with extreme care certain propositions which are usually assumed for the usual functions. . . . Thus a function of two real variables can be continuous in regard to x and in regard to y without being continuous in regard to the set of the two variables. . . . A memoir of Baire includes some curious results: the statement supposes certain notions on the discontinuity of a function with regard to a set of points. . . . Such examples show the subtlety of the research to which scholars today must devote themselves if they wish to plumb the notion of function. . . . These studies are in many points intimately bound up with speculations on the very notion of number. . . . It is likely that Cantor's theory of sets is on the eve of playing a useful role in problems which have not been expressly set as an application of the theory. . . . In a general way, let us admire the well-ordered systems, but let us be a little suspicious of their scholastic appearance, which runs the risk of suffocating the spirit of invention. Naturally it is not a question of denying the present importance of the theory of analytic functions, but we must not forget that they form only a very particular class of functions and we must hope that the day will come when mathematicians will elaborate theories more and more comprehensive; this will perhaps occur in the next century if the idea of function continues its evolution. But, for the moment, we are still in the nineteenth century!"

The indispensable tool already existed; as Picard had suspected, it was the theory of sets, which Jordan had dared to incorporate in his treatise on analysis at the Polytechnic School. "After Jordan came Lebesgue, and we enter on the subject of another Book," writes Bourbaki. In effect, the theory of sets, developed by Emile Borel in particular, permits the consideration of the problems of integration in an entirely novel form. For example, one of the questions asked is: "Over what set of points is it sufficient to know the finite derivative of a function in order that that function be determined within an additive constant?" It is actually not necessary that this derivative be defined for all points of the interval considered.

What is more, we shall consider not only numerical functions with numerical variables, but also numerical functions of which the variable is a member of a set of functions; this is functional analysis. We shall even consider liaisons between elements x of a certain set and elements $y = f(x)$ of another set of any nature whatever; this is general analysis. It is then necessary to study the most general sets, endow them with operations, define a metric, etc.—that is, create abstract spaces.

How is it possible to do such a job, and why do difficulties appear? To help us understand why, it is necessary to recall here the elementary notions of the theory of sets.

Since Cauchy, the expression "tends to infinity" has had a precise meaning. Let us restrict ourselves to considering the natural numbers (that is to say, the positive numbers, or better yet, numbers without signs). To say that the increasing integer n "tends to infinity" means that whatever integer N is chosen, n takes on values greater than N. Let us agree to write the sequence of integers $1, 2, 3, \cdots, n, \cdots$ "and so on indefinitely," which thus will have a precise meaning. Let us utilize this to label the points of a lattice which are located on a ray Ox of this lattice, and in a similar way the points on the ray Oy perpendicular to Ox. Let us now label the points of the lattice situated within the angle xOy, including those on Ox and Oy. If we label first the points of a row, for example, parallel to Ox, we arrive at "and so on indefinitely" without reaching the points of the other rows. But if we label them differently, say if we follow the two sides that are boundaries of the successive squares that have O for a vertex, we will indicate 1 on Ox; then 2 and 3 on Oy; then 4 on Ox; then 5, 6, 7, and 8 on Oy; then 9 on Ox; then 10, 11, $\cdots$ "and so on indefinitely." By this method all the points of the lattice are reached. The possibility of labeling all the elements of a set in this way characterizes what we call a *denumerable set*. But this example illustrates that the fundamental principle in arithmetic of counting finite sets no longer holds. That principle states: "The number to be assigned to a set is the last number used; and this number does not depend on the order in which the counting is done."

Let us replace "and so on indefinitely" by the symbol ω (the Greek letter omega). The successive ordinal numbers that we obtain by counting along rows parallel to Ox are then:

$$1, 2, 3, \cdots, n, \cdots, \omega, \omega + 1, \omega + 2, \cdots,$$

$$\omega + n, \cdots, \omega + \omega, \cdots, \omega + \omega + \omega, \cdots$$

"and so on transfinitely."

We will agree, naturally, to write $2\omega = \omega + \omega$, $3\omega = \omega + \omega + \omega$, $\cdots$, "and so on indefinitely," so that the ordinal number of the set considered (right-hand lattice on page 45), counted by rows, is ω^2. Therefore, sets which have for ordinal numbers ω, $k\omega$, ω^2 are denumerable, as are those which have for ordinal numbers ω^3, and ω^n. (It is sufficient to generalize the given example in a space of 3 or n dimensions.)

We assign to all these sets the *same cardinal number*, because we will say that two sets have the same cardinal number (or that they have the *same power*) if there exists between them a one-to-one correspondence, that is, if each element of each set corresponds to one and only one element of the other set.

We will give two examples of non-denumerable sets; that is, sets such that no labelable sequence $(u_1, u_2, u_3, \cdots, u_n, \cdots$ and so on indefinitely) will be able to contain all the elements of the sets in question.

Example 1. *The set of real numbers contained between 0 and 1 is not denumerable.*

We have to do here with numbers which, written in the system of numeration to the base 10, begin with 0. $abc\cdots$, where a, b, c $\cdots$ are numerals less than 10 but can all be 0 after a certain point. In order that two numbers so written will not correspond to the same point, we must reject certain improper forms in which all the numerals are 9 after a certain place; so that, we will write $0.35000\cdots$ and not $0.34999\cdots$. To simplify the explanation, it will be convenient to adopt a system of numeration to the base 2, rather than the one to the base 10, so that the only digits used will be 0 and 1.

Let u_1, u_2, u_3, $\cdots$, u_n, $\cdots$ and so on indefinitely, be a sequence of numbers written to the base 2. To write, in this system, a number x between 0 and 1 which is not equal to any other number of the sequence, we need only the spirit of contrariness:

If the first digit to the right of the point in u_1 is 1, we will take 0 as the first digit of x; if, in u_1, the first digit is 0, we will take 1 as the first digit of x. Thus, certainly, x will not equal u_1.

If the second digit to the right of the point in u_2 is 1, we will take 0 as the second digit of x; but if this second digit of u_2 is 0, then we will take 1 as the second digit of x. Thus, x will certainly not be equal to u_2.

Continuing in this way, if the nth digit of u_n is 1, we will take 0 as the nth digit of x; if it is 0, we will take 1 as the nth digit of x. Thus, x will not be equal to u_n. We can go on in this way indefinitely: the number x, so constructed and defined by its digits, will not be a member of the given sequence.

Therefore, the cardinal number of the set of numbers between 0 and 1 is not the cardinal number of a denumerable set. This last is called the *power of the countable set*, and it is represented by $\aleph_0$ (read "aleph-null"; $\aleph$ is the first letter of the Hebrew alphabet). The former is called the *power of the continuum*, and it is written $\aleph_1$.

Example 2. *The set of subsets of a set.*

Consider a set E, the elements of which are named by the lower-case letters a, b, c, $\cdots$. A *subset* or a *part* of the set E is a set whose elements are chosen from among those of E. The subsets themselves can be considered as the elements of a set of subsets; we thus can rise in the *scale of types*. (For example, a, b, c, $\cdots$ could be nuts; E would be a big bag of nuts; A and B, the subsets of E, could be small bags of nuts within the large bag, and we could speak of the set of small bags.) By considering all the subsets of E, we obtain the elements of the set of subsets of E, designated by $P(E)$. (We use a script letter to indicate, by our very choice of notation, that we have risen in the scale of types.) We are to compare the power of the set E with the power of the set $P(E)$.

Let us restrict ourselves to the example where E is the set of natural numbers. A subset A of E will contain, for instance, the numbers 2, 4, and 5. Let us agree to associate this subset with the number a, written in the system with base 2 as $0.010110000\cdots$. (The *fourth* digit of a is 1, because the number 4 belongs to A, etc.) Similarly, every subset of E, whether it contains a finite or an infinite number of elements of E, will be paired with a number between 0 and 1 by this procedure—the kth digit being 0 if k does not belong to the subset, and 1 if k does belong to the subset.

Thus, to each subset of E corresponds a number between 0 and 1.

Conversely, every number between 0 and 1 is by this procedure made to correspond to a subset of E. Therefore $P(E)$ has the power of the continuum.

Let us note that the set of numbers y between 0 and any number d can be put into a one-to-one correspondence with the set of numbers x between 0 and 1 by the homothetic relation: $y = dx$. The two sets therefore have the same power, the power of the continuum: a segment of length d therefore has the same number of points as a segment of length 1.

Let us pause here in our discussion of the preliminaries of the theory of the power of sets. It is clear that our processes of reason-

ing are not those of elementary arithmetic. Can we already antici-
pate difficulties?

One of the first contradictions arose in 1895 and troubled
Cantor, the creator of the theory of sets. He had considered "the
set of all sets." Now this idea cannot be entertained, for such a set
would have to contain itself as an element. We can see the impossibility of this if we think of the scale of types: a set is of a higher
type than any of its elements (a box of nuts is not a nut even if it
contains only one nut). Think of a catalogue which would purport
to list all catalogues; it is impossible, because this catalogue itself
could not be found among the catalogues bound together! We can
see the necessity of delimiting the object that we are reasoning
about: we must know what is meant by a set, and we must know
the forms of valid reasoning. But as Lebesgue wrote, "The results
obtained by Cantor had already [toward 1900] so transformed
thinking that these contradictions were called paradoxes—which
sounds ever so much less disturbing."

Logic itself has to be examined. For finite collections, the characteristic reasoning of arithmetic is reasoning by recurrence: if a
property, true for $n = 1$, can be proved for $n = p$ on the sole condition of being true for $n = p - 1$, it is true for any n. This procedure cannot yield a conclusion for omega, because $\omega - 1$ has no
meaning. We must therefore employ a transfinite recurrence: If a
property is true for $n = 1$, and if it is true for a number provided it
is true for all numbers that precede it, it is true for all numbers.
"This is a profound transformation," wrote Lebesgue. "It has
shocked no one, no one has even noticed it, so natural, indispensable
and inevitable does it seem. . . . Here, still, we find subjects for
both study and reasoning at the same time. . . . Thanks to this
reasoning by transfinite recurrence, the theory of denumerable sets
has been developed with the same simplicity and the same beauty
as that of the integers."

What is necessary in order to apply transfinite recurrence to
any set? Let E be such a set: it is necessary, of course, that it be
ordered in such a way that the word "precede" may have meaning.
Let F be a subset whose elements possess the property in question,

and let G be the subset consisting of members that follow those of F. We can assert the property for the first element of G; but it is necessary that this first element exist! We say a set is *well-ordered* if each of its subsets has a *first* element (that is, one that is smaller than all the others). In such a case, transfinite recurrence is applied without any difficulty. The set of real numbers between 0 and 1 is not well-ordered by the natural order, but isn't it possible to invent a relation of order whereby the set would become well-ordered? In other words, is this set well-orderable? Let us quote Lebesgue again: "Why not give the theory of sets, in general, the benefit of the same advantage (*i.e.*, the possibility of reasoning by transfinite recurrence)? It is at that point that Zermelo proclaimed that all sets could be well-ordered, and then the fat was in the fire! Two opposing camps were formed, pro and con. . . . No discussion was possible between them, because they did not have a common logic. It was logic itself that was under discussion."

Fifty years have passed. The axiom of Zermelo is so useful, actually so indispensable, in the construction of theories that it cannot be rejected in spite of the resistance of our intuition. It is in a way the reverse of the ancient attitude toward the parallel postulate: it is so intuitive that it is difficult to doubt it. As happened with the parallel postulate, Zermelo's axiom was transformed into equivalent statements, some of which have a less frightening aspect. Such for example is Hartog's statement of the problem in 1915: "Given any two sets, at least one of these has the same power as a subset of the other." Zermelo himself showed that his axiom was the equivalent of being able to *choose* an element in *every* subset F of *any* set E. For this reason it is called the *axiom of choice*. The fact that these assertions are equivalent shows sufficiently to what extent there is a counter-indication to attribute intuitive and vague meanings to the words which are useful in them. Henri Poincaré had already warned, "One has to take sides on this question." But mathematicians took care to distinguish, in their proofs, the results that came from Zermelo's axiom and those that were independent of it. They tried to prove without it what had been proved by using it; and sometimes they succeeded. Could this be done in all cases? No contradictions occurred anywhere. Moreover, as L. H. Loomis points out, Gödel was able to prove that "if mathematics is non-contradictory without the axiom of choice, it will remain non-contradictory if this axiom is added. In other words, a theorem that is proved by utilizing this axiom cannot be proved to be false, unless mathematics contains a contradiction independent of the axiom of choice." The same holds true for another celebrated axiom, one called the hypothesis of the continuum: "all non-denumerable sets of real numbers have the powers of the continuum."

In conclusion, we see what characterizes modern mathematics: Under the compulsion of the needs of physics and of the development of its own research, mathematics has become conscious of its power to create new entities by adapting to them specialized reasonings. These reasonings, therefore, are not an intuition of the senses directly inspired by the material world but rather a secondary intuition, born of familiarity with the new entities which their spirit combines and recombines by abstract manipulations replacing those of the hand. This extreme freedom, only recently acquired, is visible in all directions: the creation of new numbers for which, for instance, multiplication is not even either commutative or associative, and of numbers which even surpass infinity! The creation of new spaces of n dimension or even of an infinite number of dimensions within which displacements are defined. Distances obeying a variety of laws, in which surfaces have relations not realizable in our space! The creation of functions which bear no resemblance to the "continuous function" of Euler or to common sense! The creation of algebraic entities, analytic or even *contingent*, used to construct theories which extend, by means of merely a few additional symbols, the classical theories of ordinary number and space.

To quote Bourbaki:

"In the discussions that these theories arouse we recognize, as in all great epochs in the history of mathematics, the perpetual conflict between the men of research who are concerned with going ahead even at the risk of some insecurity, convinced that there will always be time later to consolidate the conquered territory, and the critical spirits who, though not necessarily conceding anything to the first group either in intuitive faculties or inventive talent, do not believe it lost labor to expend some effort on precise expressions and in a vigorous justification of their concepts."

It is for such preoccupation that axiomatics was constructed: for example, Hilbert sketched the outlines of an axiomatic exposition of elementary mathematics as early as 1902. Since then, one of the subjects of study for mathematicians has been the comparison of the various possible axiomatizations of the same theory, and a comparison of the concepts which are thus introduced into parallel constructions of the same theory. It is a return to the attempts of Euclid and Eudoxus, but modernizing these attempts to satisfy the new needs of mathematics.

IV

Mathematics is a science in which we never know what we are talking about nor whether what we say is true.

—BERTRAND RUSSELL

SOME ASPECTS OF METAMATHEMATICS: LOGIC AND METHODS

Mathematics resembles only slightly the formal game that laymen picture as its essence: namely, (1) starting with a list of undefined, primitive words, (2) setting forth rules for combining these words and defining new ones, and (3) applying these rules. To reduce mathematics to such a mechanical system is to misunderstand the characteristics that make it at once a science and an art; it is to throw out all the human elements—the sense of beauty, the imagination that inspires questions and directs constructions toward foreseen ends, the intuition and flair that stem from a sharp sensibility. It is to confuse the canvas with the picture, as one would say in reply to Maurice Denis's celebrated description of a painting (". . . a plane surface covered with colors arranged in a certain order").

The picture that scholars have of their science is reflected in their works. Many have prefaced their works with simple and lucid expositions of the spirit and attitude that animated their research. Mathematicians, though passionately dedicated to their science, are far from agreeing upon its nature and its purpose. We shall begin with a few quotations of opposing points of view on the foundations of mathematics.

The Question of Foundations

The evolution of the modern concepts is illuminatingly discussed in a study by Bouligand and Desgranges entitled *The Decline of Mathematico-Logical Absolutes,* and in *Conversations in Zurich,* a collection of reports on the 1938 discussions edited and annotated by Gonseth.

Let us cite a few texts that present the issues. At one extreme, Brouwer, the leader of the Intuitionist School, writes in *Formal Methods in Mathematics:* "Let us descend to the deepest level of our consciousness and let us agree that at the beginning there is only a dream-world; that, in this dream-world, the pragmatic world takes shape only by means of the phenomenon of discernment, which creates the thinking man, and the phenomenon of cunning, which creates the acting man, the combination of these phenomena engendering the external world and its objects. Now let us give the name 'game' to any activity done for its own sake and not caused by fear, desire or vocation. Let us take up the existence of the 'logical game,' which, in thinking, replaces perceived objects with fictitious and purely evocative objects, and of the 'mathematical game,' which makes a complete abstraction of the fictitious objects. The two games, by virtue of their origin, influence each other. By their nature they ought not to meddle with social life. Nevertheless, since the latter has claimed them, they are undergoing the influence of the pragmatic sciences, at the same time cooperating in the transformations of social life which are called progress. Happily, their finest developments will probably never have any connection with technical questions, either economic or political."

As a champion of the opposite view we can cite the nineteenth-century mathematician and student of mechanics Boussinesq, who devoted himself to research "in mathematics as it lives in creation, or if you prefer, in the traces left in nature by the Geometer who regulated it in producing it."

Between these two extreme positions, Fréchet presents ideas

which are fairly widely accepted: "Each branch of mathematical science—arithmetic, algebra, geometry, mechanics, the calculus of probabilities, etc.—includes four parts: 'inductive synthesis,' which leads from observation to abstraction; the 'axiomatic stage' wherein, from the results of this inductive synthesis, is disengaged the set of definitions and axioms that will serve as points of departure for the 'deductive theory'; the 'theory' itself; and finally, the 'set of experimental verifications' which follows this theory." Fréchet adds: "We recognize as tenable, though we do not agree with it, the position that the three parts other than the deductive theory are outside the proper sphere of mathematics, or at least of mathematicians." Fréchet goes on to claim for the mathematician "the right to create in the abstract some new notions which are not necessarily formed in the image of facts encountered in the world of the senses."

The right of creation is claimed by all, but differences appear in the manner of using it. The modern tendency is to demand the greatest liberty. Some mathematicians justify their work by success in applying it—*e.g.*, in the design of a new type of airplane. Others think chiefly of furnishing a tool useful in theories of physics—an aim already very far from experience. A whole school considers a work valid if it is adjudged beautiful and true by the mathematicians whom the school considers qualified, and the work is, besides, recognized as useful if it coordinates results already known or suggests others—in short, if it is useful to mathematics itself as an autonomous science. That shows a beautiful and productive courage. In any case, must we not recognize that the distinction between intrinsic interest and utility bears more upon the mathematician than upon his work? How can we foresee what will be useful in the future for physics or even for technology?

It can be maintained that whatever his aims may be, when the mathematician acts like one he loses sight of inductive syntheses and applications; he starts off from the conclusions of the former and has put into mathematized form the demands of the latter. All mathematicians, in this view, do similar work, recognized as being of a mathematical nature: all use an axiomatic and a logic, and all put to use similar forces—intuitions of fields to explore, a sense of harmony which makes them hope for certain results, an imagination which suggests generalizations allowing the unification of diverse theories or the coordination of scattered results, an astuteness which manufactures exceptional cases that serve to delimit the exact bearings of the demonstrations, and a boldness which departs from commonly accepted ideas in order to create from whole cloth a new theory. As Lebesgue has put it: "No discovery has ever been made in mathematics, or anywhere else for that matter, by an effort of deductive logic; it results from a work of creative imagination which builds what seems to be truth, guided sometimes by analogies, sometimes by an esthetic ideal, but which does not hold at all on solid logical bases. Once the discovery is made, logic intervenes to act as a control; it is logic that ultimately decides whether the discovery is really true or is illusory; its role therefore, though considerable, is only secondary."

All mathematicians, whatever their tendencies, will admit this. For example, André Weil, telling how he discovered a certain theorem of algebraic geometry, wrote: "It is thus that I became persuaded of the truth of the abstract theorem even before becoming aware of the connection between. . . . No one with any experience in the matter can fail to recognize the force of this argument, even though no proof can be based upon it." Nevertheless, the work cannot be considered finished at this point; Lebesgue reminds us that "from the viewpoint of strict knowledge, a demonstration does not exist if it is unfinished."

Even today, however, not all mathematicians agree on the degree of rigor required for the admission of certain results as mathematical truths. Thus the Italian school in algebraic geometry adopts an attitude which may seem very tolerant. Severi distinguishes two kinds of rigor, one of which may seem very subjective. In a talk at a colloquium on algebraic geometry at Liége in 1949, he compared his attitude to that of Poncelet, appealing to Poncelet's principle of continuity: "If it had been possible at that time to give a precise statement of it as of an intuitive fact to be proved later, its use would have been perfectly legitimate, for the principle would have become an axiom with an effective field of applicability, as was shown by the very correct applications Poncelet made. Thus demands of rigor would have been satisfied, as they are when, in Peano's witty phrase, one swears in court 'the whole truth and nothing but the truth.' I might call this rigor *substantive,* to differentiate it from the *formal* rigor which demands each time an axiomatic systematization from alpha to omega." At the Pisa Congress in 1948 Severi had advised leaving aside occasionally the critical analysis of the "very sure" foundations: "This certainly has its source in the conformity of the conclusions of scientists deriving from a common intuition and from the always coherent results of the use of that intuition."

This common intuition, this justification by results, we must accept insofar as principles are concerned, but the progress of mathematics pushes it lower and lower, and opposed to the opinion of the Italian school stands the modern requirement, expressed as follows by André Weil: "Rigor is no longer considered a kind of cramping formal dress which one wears for state occasions and takes off with relief upon returning home. We no longer ask whether a theorem has been rigorously proved, but whether it has been proved." To this Severi replied with a smile: "I wish to repeat the words of a young and very capable French geometer, Samuel, for he formulates a forecast corresponding to my eager wish for an even more intimate union between our geometric spirit and abstract algebra: 'A whole line of researchers, from Dedekind and Weber to Chevalley, Weil, Zariski and their pupils, has shown that it is possible to apply to algebraic geometry the methods of abstract algebra. It has also happened that many results obtained by flashes of intuition on the part of privileged Italians could be demonstrated by the rigorous methods of algebra; thus, little by little, the distrust felt by algebraists toward the Italian methods was tempered; the time is perhaps not so far off when a universal method of translation will permit the introduction, without changing the general ideas, of every so-called Italian demonstration into the rigorous framework of algebra.' "

This quotation shows clearly the trend of present-day work in mathematics. Let us concede to Picard that "it is not necessary to mutilate the human spirit in the search for truth by a sterile and ridiculous exclusivism," but let us also accept the requirement of a science more and more on the alert.

Returning to Euclid's idea, a whole school of mathematicians considers the elaboration of the axiomatic method as part of mathematics; others are not interested in it at all, but have intuitive confidence in bases which are not made explicit, and they, in effect, profit by the work of the first. But the work of axiomatization presupposes a preliminary study of logic. Although Jean Dieudonné (who, as Chatelet has written, is not completely dissociated from Bourbaki!) could say that everybody's everyday logic is used, still the *Elements* of Bourbaki had to devote its first chapter to "A Description of Formal Mathematics"; similarly, Chatelet's *Modern Arithmetic and Algebra* begins with "Notes and Vocabulary of Reasoning." One can certainly read Bourbaki by referring only to the résumé of notations and results that preceded the first book, which shows that a preliminary study of logic is not essential to comprehension for anyone who already knows how to reason. But the possibility of surmounting obstacles is no denial of their existence.

What is more, logic has itself become algebraic in becoming formal. The symbols it introduces supply a particularly clear and concise language for the most automatic part of the theory—the part we might think of as being entrustable to a machine. Thus writing in a living language is reserved for the expression of thought for the psychological and human element, a distinction eminently favorable to communication with the reader. Is this distinction purely pedagogic? Gonseth says, "The formalizing intent is the intention of making objectively explicit the moments which are only implicit in such or such a mathematical dialectic. . . . To what extent is a dialectic suitable to that which it intends to grasp and express? And to what extent is a formalism equivalent to the dialectic whose structure it claims to show? These questions bring us to the fundamental problem of knowledge, to the problem of the agreement of the thought with the object of the thought, to the problem of the simultaneous and conjoined equivalence and nonequivalence of the sign and of the thing indicated. . . . One must consider both an unformalized theory and the formalization of that theory as legitimate, provided each of them is established in coherent fashion within its own climate of evidence, for the evidences which they invoke and which they recognize are not exactly the same for both."

The Exposition of Mathematics

In what language should—or can—mathematics be set forth? In *Zurich Conversations* Skolem declared: "Clearly, when one thinks for his own benefit but says nothing to others, one is not obliged to think in formal terms. But as soon as one wishes to communicate his thought to another he must use language, and therefore he is already engaged in a formalization. The distinction between a natural language and a formal language is not a difference in principle but only a difference in degree of formalization, the formal language being constructed in a precise fashion."

In the discussion that followed, Gonseth, who presided over the Zurich meeting, summarized the ideas of Bernays: "He considers it a great discovery of logistics to have realized that, in the very broad and varied field of its activities, mathematical thought uses basically only a rather limited number of forms of reasoning, and to have discovered the means of representing these forms by the use of concrete symbols. . . . But on the other hand he believes that for the construction of a formalization the directives of intuition remain preponderant, that one cannot make abstractions of goals and meanings, and, to say it all in a word, it is denaturing mathematics to see in it only the object of syntactic considerations." And Jörgensen made this thought more precise: "A symbolism not interpreted is only a game of signs; it is a language only if it takes on meaning and if one has the use of an interpretation of the symbols and of the symbolic game; . . . the problem of the role of intuition cannot be sidestepped."

Since an exposition is made to transmit a thought from one

individual to another, the psychological factor intervenes; it is certain that the activity of thinking is diverse, the images or symbols used being no doubt different in different minds. Thus every text, not excepting mathematical texts, utilizes *several languages* in the course of the exposition. Even if we consider that a sufficiently explicit mathematical text could be expressed in a conventional language including only a small number of unchangeable words and arranged according to a syntax of very few, and inviolable, rules, human requirements would prevent complete formalization of the exposition. The *common language* brings in the gesture, the intonation, of oral transmission; it underlines the intentions, justifies the movements of the thought, warns of the dangers of misunderstanding; it is a work of art rather than of science, and properly speaking, passages written in this language are glosses and do not form part of the text itself. The *mathematical language,* technical and specialized, is used on the one hand to give the rules of formalization, and on the other hand to suggest the parts of demonstrations which are not formalized but which the reader is expected to understand because of his familiarity with the logic used and his previously acquired knowledge of the theories. It is known that mathematicians do not read but rather skim through the works of their colleagues! With a written text one must meditate, one must attempt to replace words with thoughts and to reconstruct the specific thoughts of the author. Lastly, the *formalized language* is the skeleton of the theory; it is what the teacher writes on the board, what one can check by a somewhat mechanical attention, as our experience with elementary algebra shows us; "it is why a mathematician has confidence in a colleague who transmits the result of an algebraic calculation as long as he knows that the calculation is not too long and has been done with care."

Here let us interject a parenthesis. We said that the text in common language is not part of the exposition, that the text in technical language merely suggests the thought, and now we are told that the formalized text is not, in general, read by the mathematician! Then what remains? Precisely this: when the drapery, which reveals its form more or less accurately, is torn away, there remains mathematics itself, which lives in human thought and is only symbolized by the signs of formalism. A literary text is denatured if its form is changed, but it keeps an esthetic value even if it is not understood; a mathematics text, on the other hand, has value only through the ideas which it expresses and which each reader must rethink with his own language, his own images, his own diagrams.

Each author thus has his own style, which he adapts to the supposed level of the reader. L. Schwartz writes in the introduction to his *Distributions:* "The demonstration of important theorems is done in complete detail, that of more subtle and secondary theorems more rapidly; occasionally this leads us to give a detailed demonstration of the simple and just a sketch of the difficult—a paradoxical procedure, but the advantage is greater clarity in the exposition and an easier view of the whole."

But what shall we say of mathematical language itself?

"Although once we thought that each branch of mathematics depended on a particular intuition that supplied it with primitive notions and truths, which would have made necessary for each branch a formalized language which belonged to it alone, today we know that *it is possible, logically speaking, to derive almost all of present-day mathematics from a single source, the Theory of Sets.* It will suffice therefore to set forth the principles of one single formalized language, to indicate how one can write in this language the Theory of Sets, then to show how from this theory grow one by one the different branches of mathematics as our attention turns to them. . . . Thus written in accord with the axiomatic method, and keeping always present as a sort of horizon the possibility of a total formalization, our treatise aims at a perfect rigor. . . . It is in the same realistic spirit that we contemplate here the question of non-contradiction, one of those questions which have most occupied modern logicians and which are partly at the origin of the creation of formalized languages. In the demonstration of relative non-contradiction, the metamathematical part of the reasoning is so simple that it seems scarcely possible to doubt it without renouncing all rational use of our intellectual faculties."

It is no doubt obvious that we have taken these lines from the introduction to Chapter I of Book I of the First Part of the *Elements* of Bourbaki! We refer the reader to it, as well as to the introductions and the historic notes that precede and follow each chapter. But it is impossible not to stop and speak for a minute about that illustrious mathematician Nicolas Bourbaki, "Rector magnificus of the University of Nancago" (in the phrase of the young students who edited one of Laurent Schwartz's courses at the University of Paris).

Bourbaki

Bourbaki, as is now well known, is the name not of a person but of a secret society. A considerable work requiring many years could be conceived and undertaken only in the enthusiasm of youth, in the joy of a strength conscious of itself and confident of the future, and in the secrecy of a firm comradeship.

Let us read an account of an earlier movement, reminiscent of the spirit of Bourbaki.

"It was decreed in heaven that on a sunny Sunday, the twenty-first of May, 1854, in the full spring of youth and of the year, seven poets were to meet in the castle of Font-Ségugne. . . . At the table they talked, as was customary with them, of what was needed to rescue our idiom from the desuetude in which it had lain since the time the ruling classes, betraying the honor of Provence, had reduced it, alas, to domesticity. And then, considering that from the last two congresses nothing had emerged which foretold agreement; that, on the contrary, the reforms proposed by the young men of the Avignon school had been, in the eyes of many, both badly received and badly intended, the Seven of Font-Ségugne solemnly and with one mind decided to form a separate group and, having the goal in hand, to launch the work in the desired direction.

" 'Only,' observed Glaup, 'since we are a new group, we need a new name—and more—a new emblem!' I took the floor: 'St. Anselm read and wrote . . . with the seven Félibres of the law.' 'The seven Félibres of the law! That means us!' shouted those at the table. 'Félibres let it be!' And then Glaup continued, 'That's not all, col-

leagues. We are the seven Félibres of the law . . . but the law—
who shall make it?' 'I,' I answered. 'And I vow to you that if I
have to spend 20 years of my life on it, I intend, in order to show
that our language *is* a language, to draw up the articles of law
which will govern it!'

"Odd! It seems a fairy tale, yet from that, from the vow made
on that holiday, that day of poetry and the intoxication of ideas,
emanated the colossal and fascinating task of the *Treasury of the
Félibrige*, the dictionary of the Provençal tongue into which melted
20 years of a poet's career. It was at that meeting, properly called
memorable and now shaded into legend, that was decided the publication of the collection which would be the banner of our poetry,
the standard of our idea, the bond of union among Félibres, the
communication of the Félibrige with the people. The Félibrige was
far from engendering melancholy and pessimism. Everything was
done with joy of heart, with no ulterior motive of profit or glory.
The collaborators had all taken pen names."

This passage from Mistral's charming *Mémoires*, gathered under the title *My Roots*, tells the true story of the birth of the
Félibrige.

Perhaps some day we shall also know the truth about the origin of the illustrious mathematician Nicolas Bourbaki. All we know
is that at a date reasonably near 1930 some pupils of exceptional
ability and some researchers of the École Normale Supérieure of
Ulm Street, familiar with the modern mathematics (which had developed chiefly in foreign lands after the loss of so many Frenchmen
in the War of 1914–18) and filled with the new spirit, decided
to write a treatise on *Analysis* which would translate the living
mathematical thought better than the decades-old works at hand.
Whatever their plans may have been at the beginning, since an
essential part of their task was to assure foundations acceptable
for the new requirements of rigor their work had to go beyond the
original preliminary *Books* and little by little extend to all of
mathematics.

Just as the Félibres not only stabilized a language but also
employed it to create a poetic work, so the Bourbaki group, by

choosing a language and an axiomatic, had both to explain the existing mathematics and fundamental theories and to utilize this language and these theories to enrich the science with original research. The first task was to establish a universal value. It was not to represent the opinion of one personality, however great—the authority of one man could not guarantee a doctrine acceptable for all. Therefore the work had to be collective. We can imagine the discussions, the criticisms, the retouchings that must have been necessary to achieve the work, which book by book has been presented to the world. And all this work remains secret and anonymous. If the work is valid, it must be accepted on its own; if the mathematical language is well made and responds to present needs, it will be spoken by those who feel those needs; if the construction is well supported, it will be accepted by the young mathematicians who wish to be initiated into the thinking that guided the architects. The work will prove its efficacy in use.

To this anonymous part of their work the members of the group add their personal work, this time under their own names. They then use the language and the structures they have stabilized, and thus prove the fertility of their work by surpassing it. Lastly, certain works are signed by both Bourbaki and a specific name (these names are now famous) when it is a question of studies on the margin of the treatise, such as the construction of examples justifying delicate distinctions the necessity for which might not have been apparent. The preponderant share of labor by one of the associates therefore requires in simple justice that the name of the "faithful adjutant" who performed it be revealed. It is delightful to see Nicolas Bourbaki publicly thank his "devoted secretary" (Preface to Second Edition, Chapter I, Book III), and dedicate his seventeenth pamphlet to the memory of the editor Enrique Freymann, who had had confidence in him. Thus we see that Nicolas Bourbaki has not only a good head but a good heart; one feels this also in reading the prefaces, the historic notes, and the treatise itself. It is said that punctuality is the politeness of kings; one might say that care in presentation is the politeness of authors.

But why this odd name? The N, standing for any integer, was inevitable and it apparently became Nicolas by specification! As for the name Bourbaki, it appears certain that it originally belonged to a character in farce and found its way into schoolroom slang as a hoax; there are various anecdotes about how this happened. One is that an absent-minded student, not having heard the name of the author to whom the teacher had attributed a formula, asked a fellow student: "Whose theorem?" "Bourbaki's," was the answer. But why seek a reason for the society's choice of this particular name? A name is needed! A similar incident befell a group of painters around 1890 who became known as the Nabis, according to Dorival, "because it was this Hebrew name proposed by one of their friends that these artists adopted! . . . Perhaps simply in playful irony, or by chance, or because since a group needs a name in order to have a personality one might as well choose a name strange and impressive and without great sense."

Bourbaki is young and he will remain so. He is young, a normal-school scholar, and wholly French; and he will protect his anonymity, veiled in legend, under the mantle of a secret society. But he is more: a young foreign student asking for directions to Nancy, the center of the movement at that time, was told, "You can count on the Bourbakist fraternity!"

The intention of the authors of *Elements of Mathematics* is revealed in the "Instructions for Use"; this takes up mathematics at its beginnings and gives complete proofs. The first section is devoted to fundamental structures. After the theory of sets, the two basic theories discussed are general algebra and general topology. Then follows a study of complex structures, in which the preceding studies are combined. This leads to a new exposition of mathematics. "The method of exposition in the first section is axiomatic and abstract: it proceeds from the general to the particular. The choice of this method is imposed by the principal objective of this section, namely, to provide a solid foundation for the rest of the treatise, and even for the complete treatment of modern mathematics."

It is clear that a book with such an ambition is not especially destined for those beginners who wish to get a superficial overview of mathematics nor for the technician who seeks to gather results and formulas rapidly in order to apply them. Rather, the fundamental discussion permits those who already have some adequate concepts of the science to examine the foundations which they had already accepted more or less intuitively and subconsciously. Moreover, the professional mathematician, or the future mathematician, will find gathered together all that he will need; the treatise serves him as a dictionary or a grammar. Its extremely concise style emphasizes the delicate points that he wishes to have clarified. This project is further facilitated by the leaflets of results, the indices of notations, the terminological indices, the fold-outs in which he can have before him the principal definitions, axioms, and essential results—and, finally, by the dictionaries. In addition, the precise cross references permit him to work on any chapter without the need of knowing beforehand all that precedes it. Finally, remarks, cautions, and exercises carefully graded according to difficulty display a constant concern with teaching (if we don't restrict this term to elementary education). Followers of Bourbaki have heard of its helpful notations, such as "Dangerous curve ahead," which young pupils in the Lycée have sometimes decorated with skull and crossbones!

The book introduces all the words and symbols necessary for an abstract exposition, but the publication itself is only slightly formalized; every paragraph uses only the symbols appropriate for the subject under discussion and the general symbols of the theory of sets. Twenty years ago, when the first *Leaflet of Results* appeared, misunderstanding might have dampened the curiosity of some who, on opening the book, saw so many cabalistic signs and so little text! It was like judging the style of a book by its table of contents.

The treatise, whose publication is continuing, is now in the libraries of the entire world, and, in spite of its linguistic peculiarities, it is cited as of first rank in all modern bibliographies.

Let us now return to discussion of the modern approach to logic and consider some examples of the Bourbaki treatment of the theory of sets; in the next chapter we shall introduce the theories of general algebra and general topology.

Logic and Symbolism

Mathematical logic is the subject of numerous studies made necessary by the new modes of reasoning in modern science. These studies answer the present need to make concepts more and more explicit and to formalize them.

In effect, complex mathematical theories can no longer be transmitted without the use of symbols—logical as well as mathematical—on which one operates in accord with strict rules. The possibility of formalization is even regarded by some as the only guarantee of the validity of a reasoning; it is necessary to modern proofs of non-contradiction, the first requirement for any axiomatization.

The experienced mathematician, who thinks more of the growth of the science than of its exposition and its justification, can be satisfied with a certain esthetic sentiment confirmed by the adherence of other mathematicians to guarantee the validity of his reasonings. When he puts these into a book, he can implicitly presuppose on the part of the reader an understanding of that logic; and whenever the need seems to arise he interpolates certain remarks—certain refinements of a metamathematical nature (to justify such expressions as "analogous conditions," "it is clear that"), or novel reasonings, for example, when he touches on the infinite.

There are here certain pedagogic imperatives, and it is no doubt legitimate to bring in such remarks more or less belatedly on such matters as "constructions in geometry" when one has been making them from the very beginning. But when one claims to be making an exposition of the totality of fundamental mathematics from which all of mathematics is to be constructed, it is necessary to examine the mathematical objects and the logic used. We have already referred to the introduction of the transfinite, to the two forms of reasoning by recurrence; we shall say no more on these difficult questions of metamathematics. We wish only to recall the simplest operations of elementary logic and to indicate its formalism—now in use in the books, especially in the mimeographed courses, in the résumés written on the blackboard by teachers and, if I may say so, in the mental diagrams in the memories of those who use the theory.

Elementary logic may be presented in two forms: if it compares qualities, attributes of objects, it is the logic of predicates or the *logic of intension*. If it directs its attention to the classes of objects that have these properties or attributes, it is the logic of sets, or classes, called *logic of extension*. The question is whether these logics are equivalent; that is to say, whether each is merely a translation of the other. In any case certain phrases remain ambiguous if one does not make clear in what sense they are to be considered; thus, if one says "a wildflower is not black," does that mean that it is incompatible for a flower to be both wild and black, or that among the known wildflowers none is black? Let's not push it; let us remember only that the language used in mathematics must not be ambiguous. This is why no assertion can be isolated but must, on the contrary, be preceded by a phrase which determines its meaning.

We are going to give some pretty exact forms, so that the translation from one logic to the other may be effectively possible; we shall then be able to choose the symbolism which is most favorable in the mathematical exposition of a theory.

Every statement will be preceded by "It is a question of objects of such and such a domain," that is, of objects more or less clearly determined but about which we shall know what attributes are permissible or impermissible. For example, when it is a question of triangles, we shall be able to qualify them as "right-angled" or "isosceles" but not as "hot" or "heavy" (something which theoretic logic does not always reject).

Logic of Intension

Sentences. A declarative sentence attributes a quality to an element of the domain. It is necessary in mathematics to distinguish between two types of sentences:

a) Let us consider the natural numbers and let us say that "5 is odd" or "6 is odd." The first of these sentences is *true*, the second is *false*.

b) The same domain: we say, "x is odd." This is true or false depending on the replacement for x. The value—"truth" or "falsehood"—of the sentence depends on the choice of the replacement for x from the domain of the integers. The sentence is a function of x; we may also call it an *open sentence* or a propositional function. The function can take on only two values: "true" or "false." In formal logic we often indicate the value *true* by the numeral "1" and the value *false* by the numeral "0." The logic that we are discussing is thus a *two-valued logic*.

Implication. An *implication* or a *conditional* between two sentences (1) and (2) is indicated by:

$$\text{Sentence (1)} \Rightarrow \text{Sentence (2)}$$

(read, "(1) implies (2)" or "If (1), then (2)"). For example, if we are discussing polygons:

$$\text{T is a triangle} \Rightarrow \text{T is convex}$$

(read, "If T is a triangle, then T is convex").

If we write the two sentences as α and $\mathcal{B}$, the implication is written as:

$$\alpha \Rightarrow \mathcal{B} \tag{I}$$

We are considering now the domain, no longer of the simple statements α and $\mathcal{B}$, but of a set of statements of a higher type. (I) is the statement "α implies $\mathcal{B}$," which, by definition, has the value "true" if α and $\mathcal{B}$ have the values "true," and which has the value "false" if α has the value "true" and $\mathcal{B}$ has the value "false." The statement (I) has *no* value and cannot be used if α has the value "false."

If (I) is true in a theory, it is a *true relation* of that theory—a theorem or, eventually, an axiom of that theory. We have, in this case, the following table of values or *truth table* (a double-entry table similar to a table of operation such as a multiplication or addition table):

$\mathcal{C}$

		1
	1	1
$\mathcal{B}$	0	0

The method of proof called *reductio ad absurdum* is the following:

1. We are testing a statement $\mathcal{C}$ which can only be either true or false;
2. We adopt the hypothesis that $\mathcal{C}$ is true in the theory under discussion;
3. We show that in this theory:

$$(I)\quad \mathcal{C} \Rightarrow \mathcal{B} \qquad \text{is true;}$$

4. An independent investigation shows that $\mathcal{B}$ is false.

A contradiction appears, for if $\mathcal{B}$ is false and $\mathcal{C}$ is true, the implication is that (I) is false, as is seen from our table. Therefore the assumption (2) that $\mathcal{C}$ is true is not tenable. Therefore $\mathcal{C}$ is false and none of the assertions obtained after (2) can be retained.*

* In this book the symbol $\Rightarrow$ is used as a tool to derive true mathematical relations from true statements. It is for this reason that we do not utilize the truth table generally used in formal logic, in which values are assigned to all possible combinations of truth values of $\mathcal{C}$ and $\mathcal{B}$, that is:

$\mathcal{C}$

		1	0
	1	1	1
$\mathcal{B}$	0	0	1

The fundamental property of the implication is *transitivity*. Consider the three implications:

(I) $\qquad\qquad\qquad\qquad \mathcal{Q} \Rightarrow \mathcal{B}$

(II) $\qquad\qquad\qquad\qquad \mathcal{B} \Rightarrow \mathcal{C}$

(III) $\qquad\qquad\qquad\qquad \mathcal{Q} \Rightarrow \mathcal{C}$

If (I) and (II) have the value "true," so has (III).

This last sentence is a new implication which can be written:

$$[(I) \text{ and } (II)] \Rightarrow (III)$$

The first member of this last implication is said to be formed by a *conjunction* of (I) and (II).

Conjunction. If $\mathcal{Q}$ and $\mathcal{B}$ are two statements in a theory, the *conjunction* of $\mathcal{Q}$ and $\mathcal{B}$ is the logical operation whereby a new statement $\mathcal{C}$ is formed whose values are defined by the following truth table (or table of operation):

		$\mathcal{Q}$	
		1	0
$\mathcal{B}$	1	1	0
	0	0	0

The conjunction of two statements $\mathcal{Q}$ and $\mathcal{B}$ is written as:

$$\mathcal{C} = \mathcal{Q} \text{ and } \mathcal{B}$$

or $\qquad\qquad\qquad\qquad \mathcal{C} = \mathcal{Q} \wedge \mathcal{B}$

Disjunction. The *disjunction* of two statements is a logical operation which, starting with two statements, $\mathcal{Q}$ and $\mathcal{B}$, forms from them a third statement $\mathcal{D}$ whose values are given by the truth table:

		$\mathcal{Q}$	
		1	0
$\mathcal{B}$	1	1	1
	0	1	0

This is written as $\mathfrak{D} = \mathfrak{A}$ or $\mathfrak{B}$

or $\mathfrak{D} = \mathfrak{A} \vee \mathfrak{B}$

(The word "or" signifies here that $\mathfrak{D}$ is "true" if *at least one* of the statements $\mathfrak{A}$ and $\mathfrak{B}$ is "true"; it is not used in the exclusive sense.)

Therefore, $\mathfrak{A} \wedge \mathfrak{B}$ can be used as the first term of a conditional if $\mathfrak{A}$ and $\mathfrak{B}$ are both true; $\mathfrak{A} \vee \mathfrak{B}$ can be used as the first term of a conditional if at least one of $\mathfrak{A}$ and $\mathfrak{B}$ is true. In particular:

$$\mathfrak{A} \wedge \mathfrak{A} = \mathfrak{A}$$

$$\mathfrak{A} \vee \mathfrak{A} = \mathfrak{A}$$

These two operations, conjunction and disjunction, are both commutative, as their respective truth tables show:

$$\mathfrak{A} \wedge \mathfrak{B} \Leftrightarrow \mathfrak{B} \wedge \mathfrak{A}$$

$$\mathfrak{A} \vee \mathfrak{B} \Leftrightarrow \mathfrak{B} \vee \mathfrak{A}$$

If the tables are repeated, we see that these operations are also associative:

$$(\mathfrak{A} \wedge \mathfrak{B}) \wedge \mathfrak{C} \Leftrightarrow \mathfrak{A} \wedge (\mathfrak{B} \wedge \mathfrak{C})$$

and $(\mathfrak{A} \vee \mathfrak{B}) \vee \mathfrak{C} \Leftrightarrow \mathfrak{A} \vee (\mathfrak{B} \vee \mathfrak{C})$

but these properties, commutativity and associativity, become more obvious when we see their translation in the logic of extension.

The Negation of a Statement. Negation is the logical operation whereby we pass, for example, from "x is odd" to "x is not odd"; or, if we use the example of the polygon, "X is a square" to "X is not a square." The negation of a statement, then, is another statement which has the value "true" if the former has the value "false," and which has the value "false" if the former has the value "true."

If a statement is designated by $\mathfrak{A}$, the negation is designated by "not $\mathfrak{A}$," or $\mathfrak{A}'$ or $\sim\mathfrak{A}$. By its definition, the negation of a negation is the original statement.

The three defined operations, conjunction, disjunction, and negation, are not independent, because we have, for example:

$$\text{not } (\mathfrak{A} \wedge \mathfrak{B}) \Leftrightarrow (\text{not } \mathfrak{A}) \vee (\text{not } \mathfrak{B})$$

This is clearly shown by means of truth tables, because the two members give operations which are defined by means of truth tables:

		Values of α	
		1	0
Values of $\mathcal{B}$	1	0	1
	0	1	1

and

		Values of α'	
		1	0
Values of $\mathcal{B}'$	1	1	1
	0	1	0

which are clearly equivalent.

We have given these illustrations to suggest the possibility of replacing the questions posed by this logic with studies of these truth tables. This is known as the method of *matrices*.

Contrapositive, Converse. A fundamental formulation is the following: All the theorems of a theory can be expressed by one or the other of the two implications which are called the *contrapositives* of each other:

$$(T) \qquad \alpha \Rightarrow \mathcal{B}$$

$$(U) \qquad \mathcal{B}' \Rightarrow \alpha'$$

For example, if we discuss polygons, α could be "x is a triangle" and $\mathcal{B}$ "x is convex." If "x is a triangle" implies "x is convex," to say that "x is not convex" implies that "x is not a triangle" and conversely.

This formulation states the *principle of the excluded middle* and it is used in the proof by *reductio ad absurdum*. We can see from the differences demonstrated by the truth tables for (T) and for (U) that we could not prove it by the theorems that precede it.

Values of (T)

		α	
		1	
$\mathcal{B}$	1	1	
	0	0	

Values of (U)

		$\mathcal{B}$	
		0	
α	0	1	
	1	0	

This is an axiom of the logic generally used (Aristotelian logic), but it is rejected by intuitionist logic, which is, therefore, clearly more demanding in its proofs.

Now, from the two statements α and $\mathcal{B}$ and their negations we can form four implications, only two of which need to be proved.

If $\alpha \Rightarrow \mathcal{B}$ is a theorem (T) of a theory, $\mathcal{B}' \Rightarrow \alpha'$ is the same theorem in the contrapositive form. If $\mathcal{B} \Rightarrow \alpha$ is also a theorem (R), then $\alpha' \Rightarrow \mathcal{B}'$ is the same theorem; (T) and (R) are called *converses* of each other. The totality of these theorems can be written in any of the following forms:

$$\alpha \Leftrightarrow \mathcal{B}$$

$$\mathcal{B} \Leftrightarrow \alpha$$

$$\alpha' \Leftrightarrow \mathcal{B}'$$

$$\mathcal{B}' \Leftrightarrow \alpha'$$

The statements α and $\mathcal{B}$ are then said to be *equivalent* in the theory.

Note: The word "equivalent" characterizes relations that have the following properties:

Reflexivity: α is equivalent to itself.
Symmetry: α is equivalent to $\mathcal{B}$ means also $\mathcal{B}$ is equivalent to α.
Transitivity: From "α is equivalent to $\mathcal{B}$," and "$\mathcal{B}$ is equivalent to $\mathcal{C}$," it follows that "α is equivalent to $\mathcal{C}$."

What we have said so far is sufficient to show how the demonstrations of elementary mathematics, at least in part, can be formalized; or, rather, that they can be schematized. We shall give examples of this in Appendix I.

Quantifiers. The logic of intension (as the logic of extension, which we are going to introduce) cannot be utilized in mathematics unless we specify the objects of the domain to which an open sentence applies. If we do not do this, we cannot formulate the theorems of the theory, because it is necessary to have a "true" value for a statement. For example, if we are discussing triangles, to say "x has three angles" is to make a statement that is true for all elements of the universe under discussion, *i.e.*, it is true no matter what replacement we make for x. But to say "x is isosceles" is to make a statement that is true only for certain elements of the universe. An open sentence cannot be used in a theory unless there is at least one element in the universe for which the statement obtained by placing this element in the open sentence is true. From this consideration we arrive at the following two concepts:

(a) *The universal quantifier:* "For every element of the domain" (designated ∀) the open sentence is true.

$$\forall x, \text{ ⟨a⟩ is true.}$$

(This is sometimes read, "for any x, the open sentence ⟨a⟩ is true.")

(b) *The existential quantifier:* "There is at least one element of the domain such that" (designated ∃) ⟨a⟩ is true.

$$\exists x, \text{ ⟨a⟩ is true.}$$

In this way we obtain finally the logic of intension, two-valued and quantified.

Logic of Extension: The Algebra of Sets

In talking of the domain we have avoided the use of the word "set." Actually, though it corresponds to the intuitive notion of a collection, a bunch or a lot, the term "set" in mathematics is reserved for things having properties which we are going to indicate and which constitute an axiomatic definition of the term.

We are still thinking of a domain or a universe; we will name the elements or members of this universe or set by the lower-case letters a, b or x; they are also called the "points" or "atoms" of the theory. Sets will be named by capital letters: E, A, B. We define in the theory a relation of an element to the universe, the relation of belonging to (or being a member of) the universe, and we use the notation:

$$a \in E, \text{ meaning "}a \text{ is a member of E"}$$

The negation of this statement is:

$$a \notin E, \text{ meaning "}a \text{ is not a member of E"}$$

The relation of the *inclusion* of a set A in a set E is the relation defined by:

$$\forall x, [x \in A] \Rightarrow [x \in E]$$

which is read, "for every element x of the universe, the statement 'x is a member of A' implies 'x is a member of E.'"

This relation is indicated in symbols by:

$$A \subseteq E \quad \text{or} \quad E \supseteq A,$$

and it is read, "A is included in E."

Now we can define three operations on sets: complementation, intersection, and union.

Complementation. If A is included in E, the *complement* of A with respect to E, (which is written, $\mathbf{C}_E A$) is defined by:

$$\forall x, x \in E, [x \notin A \Rightarrow x \in \mathbf{C}_E A]$$

If no ambiguity results, we can indicate the complement by $\mathbf{C}A$, without a subscript, or even A'. By definition we then can say:

$$(A')' = A$$

Passing from A to its complement is an operation in the logic of sets which corresponds to negation in the logic of intension.

The *intersection* ($\cap$) of two sets is the operation which associates to any two sets A and B (defined in the same universe), a set J by the relation of which the first member is the conjunction of two statements:

$$\forall x, [(x \in A) \wedge (x \in B)] \Leftrightarrow (x \in J)$$

This operation is indicated in symbols by:

$$J = A \cap B$$

Therefore, *intersection* in the theory of sets corresponds to *conjunction* in the logic of intension.

The *union* ($\cup$) of two sets A and B of the same universe is the operation whereby to every pair of sets A and B we associate a set R defined by:

$$\forall x, [(x \in A) \vee (x \in B)] \Leftrightarrow (x \in R)$$

That is to say, R consists of the elements which belong to A, or to B, or to both.

The operation "union" therefore corresponds to *disjunction* in the logic of statements.

The three operations, thus defined, are not independent, for if A and B are included in E, then

$$A \cup B = \mathbf{C}(\mathbf{C}A \cap \mathbf{C}B),$$

or, using the alternate notation for the complement:

$$A \cup B = (A' \cap B')'$$

There is a model which pictures these operations upon sets concretely by means of a diagram called the Venn diagram. In this diagram the elements of the universe are represented by points in a plane (or a rectangle) and the elements of a set, E, A, B, are represented by the points in the interior of a closed curve without multiple points. For example, in the illustration below we show the two subsets A and B which are included in a set E; the doubly-shaded region represents the intersection A ∩ B, and the whole region with some form of shading is the union A ∪ B.

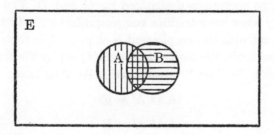

By the help of such diagrams it is easy to see the obvious properties (which we must take as axioms of the theory). Union and intersection are both commutative operations:

$$A \cup B = B \cup A, \quad A \cap B = B \cap A$$

moreover:
$$A \cup A = A \quad \text{and} \quad A \cap A = A$$

By constructing a similar diagram for three subsets of E (using colors or shadings for the various regions) we find that union and intersection are both associative operations.

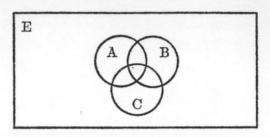

$$(A \cup B) \cup C = A \cup (B \cup C)$$

and $\quad\quad\quad (A \cap B) \cap C = A \cap (B \cap C)$

We can also ascertain that each operation is distributive with respect to the other:

$$A \cup (B \cap C) = (A \cup B) \cap (A \cup C)$$

and $\quad\quad\quad A \cap (B \cup C) = (A \cap B) \cup (A \cap C)$

It should be noted that these properties do not distinguish between the two operations designated by $\cup$ and $\cap$. The distinction appears only when we introduce complementation: in fact, the intersection of a set with its complement is empty, while their union is E (the universe) itself. We designate the empty set by the Scandinavian letter $\emptyset$ (read, "null set," "empty set"). We then have:

$$A \cap A' = \emptyset$$

$$A \cup A' = E$$

Moreover:

$$A \cup \emptyset = A \quad \text{and} \quad A \cap \emptyset = \emptyset$$

and finally,

$$A \cup E = E \quad \text{and} \quad A \cap E = A$$

$$\emptyset' = E$$

The set of subsets A, B, $\cdots$, L of E is said to be provided with the structure of a Boolean algebra. The name comes from George

Boole, the creator of the logic of extension (*An Investigation of the Laws of Thought*, 1854), which is the most fundamental example of an algebra having such a structure.

An *expression* in Boolean algebra is an indication of the operations to be performed, in the algebra of sets, that will result in a set. The properties of the operations permit us to simplify them. For example:

$$X = (A \cap B)' \cap (A \cup B) = (A' \cup B') \cap (A \cup B)$$

$$= (A \cap B') \cup (A' \cap B)$$

It is important from the point of view of logic (even more than from the point of view of pure mathematics) to have a regular and automatic procedure whereby we can determine whether two Boolean expressions are equal. This can be achieved because of the uniqueness of certain expressions which are called *canonical forms*. (In this context canonical forms might be comparable to writing an algebraic expression without denominators as a polynomial in which similar terms have been combined and arranged in order.)

To define canonical forms let us make use of Venn diagrams. Every subset X can be considered—and in only one way—as the union of the least parts determined by the subsets A, B, $\cdots$, L which appear in the expression; parts, moreover, which are disjoint two by two and whose union is E. (We say that they constitute a *partition* of E.) Let us call such subsets *elementary subsets*. They are expressed as intersections of the elements A, B, $\cdots$, L of the expression, or of their complements. Thus for two letters, A and B, there are four elementary subsets:

$$A \cap B, \quad A \cap B', \quad A' \cap B, \quad A' \cap B'.$$

For three letters, A, B, and C, the diagram will show eight elementary subsets:

$A \cap B \cap C$	$A' \cap B' \cap C'$
$A' \cap B \cap C$	$A \cap B' \cap C'$
$A \cap B' \cap C$	$A' \cap B \cap C'$
$A \cap B \cap C'$	$A' \cap B' \cap C$

Given an expression, simple calculation enables us to express it as the union of these elementary subsets. Returning to our first example, we find:

$$X = (A \cap B)' \cap (A \cup B) = (A \cap B') \cup (A' \cap B)$$

In this way X has been put into the canonical form for the two letters A and B.

If X occurs in an expression which contains another letter C, this must be introduced. We can do this by means of the equality:

$$X = (X \cap C) \cup (X \cap C')$$

The theorem on unique representation is utilized in statistics to compare data involving a large number of subsets. (For example, the members of a population may be classified as healthy milk-drinkers, old and sickly ones, young wine-drinkers, young unhealthy milk-drinkers, etc.; these groups must be clarified and made comparable to other groups.)

But the theorem is of particular interest from the logical point of view when we return to the logic of intension. Deduction in the logic of intension corresponds to inclusion in the logic of extension—and this can be expressed by the equality of Boolean expressions.

In fact, if A is the set of objects of the domain which have the property $\mathcal{C}$, and B the set of objects of the same domain which have the property $\mathcal{B}$, the implication:

$$\mathcal{C} \Rightarrow \mathcal{B}$$

is logically equivalent to:

$$\forall x, x \in A \Rightarrow x \in \mathcal{B}$$

that is to say:

$$A \subseteq B$$

(A is a subset of B)

Now this is expressed by:

$$A = A \cap B$$

or

$$B = A \cup B$$

or, better still, under canonical form:

$$A \cap B' = \varnothing$$

The result is that, by algebraic calculation which can be entrusted to a machine, we can determine whether two assertions in elementary (Aristotelian) logic are equivalent. By putting them in canonical forms, we can clarify situations which are complicated by various conditions. This is actually done in practice in certain problems concerning life insurance.

Connection between the Logics of Intension and Extension

The connection between the two elementary logics is made when we pose the question: "Consider the set A of elements of the domain which have the property α." This phrase is meaningful if α is a *collectivizing property*, *i.e.*, if it makes possible distinguishing in the domain the elements x which belong to A from the elements y which do not belong to A:

$$x \in A \quad \text{and} \quad y \notin A \Leftrightarrow y \in \mathbf{C}A$$

This can give rise to some very serious difficulties. In the first place, it may be that no element of the domain makes α true—we have already noted that in such a case the set A is the *empty set*, $A = \varnothing$. Then every element of the domain is such that "not α" is true in the theory:

$$\forall x, \text{ "not } \alpha\text{" is true} \tag{1}$$

We can show, on the contrary, that A is not empty by proving that there exists at least one element of the domain which makes α true:

$$\exists x, \alpha \text{ is true} \tag{2}$$

But the controversial case is the one in which, in a theory, neither (1) nor (2) can be proved.

If we ignore the question whether these statements are provable, we can speak of the set A as the hypothesis of the investigation. If (1) is true, we are often led to modify the theory so that α might become collectivizing by adding to the domain new elements, constructed axiomatically with the aid of $\mathcal{C}$. We shall return later to this essential procedure in extending a theory.

If (2) is proved, A is not empty. But other difficulties arise almost immediately: We might say, "let x be an element of A; by the operations of the theory, we deduce from this $f(x)$, etc." In order that this may have a precise meaning, it is necessary to postulate implicitly a procedure whereby the element x can be distinguished from the other elements of A. This offers no difficulty if, for example, A contains only a finite number of elements or if it is denumerable. But for many very general sets this is a form of the *axiom of choice*, and the conditions under which it is valid are a matter of serious discussion.

When one has been able to express the content of a theory in the language of the logic of extension, the symbolism is unambiguous and the formalization is clearer than in the logic of intension. Many statements of definitions and theorems are now given in the language of sets under particularly clear forms; we shall give examples of these in our chapter devoted to pedagogy.

Comparison of Theories: Models

Equivalent Theories. If two theories $\mathfrak{I}$ and $\mathfrak{I}'$ are such that every element in the domain of each is associated to an element in the domain of the other (one-to-one correspondence), and if every operational or relational sign of one is similarly associated with a sign of the other, and if every true relation in one is translated by a true relation in the other—if all these conditions obtain, we say that the two theories define in their domains an *isomorphic* correspondence. For the mathematician the two theories are two translations of a unique theory—for he is concerned only with the relations between objects and not the objects themselves. If we refer the theories, by translation, to the same domain, we obtain equivalent theories. They differ only in the method of exposition adopted. Isomorphic domains constitute *models* of the same abstract theory.

Relations between Theories. If a theory ℑ has an isomorphic image in ℑ′, but if ℑ′ has in addition elements and signs without associates in ℑ, we say that theory ℑ′ is "more powerful" than ℑ. There is then a tendency to mingle in the notation the elements and signs of ℑ with their images in ℑ′ by an "abuse of language" or an "abuse of notation." For example, the theory of signed numbers (positive and negative) is more powerful than the theory of absolute numbers (without convention of sign): we tend to confuse absolute numbers with their images, the positive numbers. Another illustration: The ordinary Euclidean metric geometry is more powerful than affine geometry (in which distance is not defined for every two points); the signs introduced in affine geometry are retained in metric geometry in such a way that every theorem of affine geometry is a theorem of metric geometry.

The richest theory is said to be a "model" of the poorest theory. If the richest theory is better known than the other, and is more intuitive, its use is naturally good for a study of the poorer theory, ℑ. But more than that, every relation which is "true" or "false" in ℑ has the same value "true" or "false" in ℑ′, so that if it is proved to be true in ℑ′, it is therefore true in ℑ. It is in this way that theorems of affine geometry are often proved in elementary geometry by considerations of metric geometry. For example, affine properties of parallelograms are proved by applying cases of the congruence of triangles. Similarly, affine geometry is a more powerful theory than projective geometry, and we often demonstrate projective theorems by utilizing the theorem of Thales, which belongs to affine geometry. We prefer, if it is possible and not too complicated, to prove a theorem by means of the theory under study, as Chasles demanded for projective geometry. But it is not always easy to determine the weakest theory in which a given theorem is true. The fact that the three altitudes of a triangle are concurrent is demonstrated in elementary geometry by means of parallel lines, and therefore by the postulate of Euclid. But the theorem is true even if we do not adopt this axiom: it is true in the geometry of Lobachevsky. This is certainly not obvious.

To prove that a property $\mathcal{P}$ is independent of the set $\mathcal{Q}$ of the axioms of a theory ℑ—*i.e.*, that ℘ does not belong to ℑ—we must construct a model, a theory in which all the axioms of ℑ (and other axioms, ultimately) are true and in which ℘ is not true. Actually, if ℘ is a part of ℑ, ℘ is true in all models in which the axioms of ℑ are true. It is in this way that the model of Poincaré proves that Euclid's axiom on the uniqueness of the parallel line does not belong to the theory defined by the axioms which precede the axiom in question.

Let us now give a few examples of isomorphic theories. We will merely indicate the beginning of the dictionary which defines the correspondence.

The first example:

Domain	Domain
The set of real numbers	The set of positive numbers
0	1
1	10
2	100
a	a'
b	b'
$a + b$	$a'b'$
(Associative, commutative)	(Associative, commutative)

From this beginning we construct the theory of logarithms.

A second example:

Points on an axis	Real numbers
Point O	Number 0
Points M, A	Numbers x, a
Translation $\left(\overrightarrow{MM'} = \overrightarrow{OA} \right)$	Addition of a ($x' = x + a$)

The addition of a is often called, by an abuse of language, a "translation" in the real numbers system. Translation in the plane is too rich a theory for the addition of a in the set of real numbers, but it is equivalent to the addition of a in the set of complex numbers.

A third example:

In metric geometry, the
three symmetries S_1, S_2, S_3
with respect to three axes
concurrent at angles of 60°

Permutations on the triplet of
three letters: a, b, c

Symmetry S_1

$$\begin{bmatrix} a \rightharpoonup a \\ b \rightharpoonup c \\ c \rightharpoonup b \end{bmatrix} \mathcal{P}_1$$

Symmetry S_2

$$\begin{bmatrix} a \rightharpoonup c \\ b \rightharpoonup b \\ c \rightharpoonup a \end{bmatrix} \mathcal{P}_2$$

Symmetry S_3

$$\begin{bmatrix} a \rightharpoonup b \\ b \rightharpoonup a \\ c \rightharpoonup c \end{bmatrix} \mathcal{P}_3$$

$S_1 \times S_2 \times S_3 = S_2$

$$\begin{bmatrix} a \rightharpoonup c \\ b \rightharpoonup b \\ c \rightharpoonup a \end{bmatrix} = \mathcal{P}_1 \times \mathcal{P}_2 \times \mathcal{P}_3 = \mathcal{P}_2$$

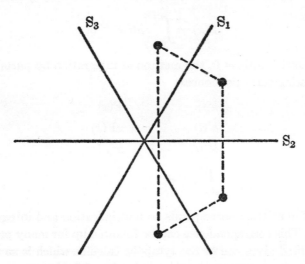

Another classic example associates to each point its polar with respect to a circle—collinear points correspond to concurrent lines.

But a model can also be a physical theory T′ whose purely physical properties naturally do not appear (it is a richer theory) but which contains the image of the mathematical theory. To illustrate:

Switches in an electric circuit	Values of a two-valued logic of intension
Switches A and B	Properties $\mathfrak{a}$ and $\mathfrak{B}$
Switch closed	Value 1
Switch open	Value 0
Connection in series	Conjunction $\mathfrak{a} \wedge \mathfrak{B}$
Connection in parallel	Disjunction $\mathfrak{a} \vee \mathfrak{B}$

This suggests the possibility of an *analogue computer* for studying complicated electrical circuits. Moreover, we have translated the logic of intension into a calculus of sets.

Another example, extremely important for certain applications, gives the possibility of translating analytical theories by means of an algebraic model. Thus, the Laplace transformation associates to a function $h(t)$ another function $F(x)$ which is given by the formula:

$$F(x) = \int_0^{+\infty} h(t)e^{-tx}\, dt$$

By letting $h(0) = 0$, the method of integration by parts gives us the following correspondences:

$h(t)$	$F(x)$
$h'(t)$	$xF(x)$
$h''(t)$	$x^2F(x)$
$\displaystyle\int_0^t h(t)\, dt$	$\dfrac{1}{x}F(x)$

Here differentiation corresponds to multiplication and integration to division. This correspondence can be followed up for many properties. This method gives rise to the symbolic calculus which is so useful in such areas as electricity and the mechanics of fluids.

These few examples illustrate well one of the most essential characteristics of modern mathematics: the fact that its abstract form is susceptible of many models therefore provides a great economy of thought.

The Extension of a Theory. The domain of a theory is enriched by creating new elements. *In the very heart of a theory,* a new element is *defined by a construction* which assures its existence and at the same time determines a set of properties characteristic of this element. All that remains is to give the element a name, and eventually a symbol. For example, knowing the theory of parallels, one can define a parallelogram. In the geometry of space, for every point A of a plane, a line perpendicular to the plane is defined. We prove that there exists a line perpendicular to two lines of the plane at the point A, then we prove that this line $x'Ax$ does not depend on the two lines chosen in P; we call this line the perpendicular to the plane at the point A, and we write $x'Ax \perp (P)$.

In the same way, we demonstrate in the arithmetic of integers the existence of a common divisor of two numbers which is greater than all other common divisors, and we call it the greatest common factor. We do not consider the definition entirely satisfactory, however, until we indicate a procedure for determining it effectively after a finite number of operations (the Euclidean algorithm): the greatest common factor is then defined by construction.

But what happens if we demonstrate the existence of an element of a theory without being able to determine it effectively by a finite number of operations? We will extend the meaning of the word "construct"; moreover, existence proofs in general allow an *approximate* determination of the defined element. Thus, by demonstrating that a series is convergent, we can obtain the sum by approximations which can be continued indefinitely. (Let us not talk of the case where it is necessary to carry them on transfinitely!)

On the other hand, the definition of an element enables us to rise from one theory to a more powerful theory, if the creation of this element gives the enlarged domain properties which the primitive domain did not possess. Therefore, a new element ought to be defined by the properties which we wish to introduce; this is *definition by axiomatization.* The only condition that is imposed is that the properties of the original domain should be retained; that is, that the newly introduced properties should be compatible with the old properties. This creation of more and more powerful theories by *extension* is the very method of the growth of mathematics. We say that the old domain is plunged or immersed in the more extended domain.

The entire history of numbers is the extension of the theory of natural integers to fractional numbers, to signed numbers, to algebraic numbers. The passage to complex numbers (imaginaries) is not an extension, unless we disregard the order relation as a requirement of the sought theory, because this relation does not hold for these numbers.

Thus the Egyptians, in order to make possible the division of a unit by an integer, say 3, invented new numbers, the unit fractions, and the notation ⌒ (for a third); but the sum of such unit fractions was not a number! The Greeks created the numbers that were missing: they needed pairs of integers (the fractions) with a relation of equivalence among them (*e.g.*, $2/3 \equiv 4/6 \equiv 6/9$). A rational number is a set of equivalent fractions.

But geometry demanded that one attribute to the equation $xx = 2$ a root which it did not possess. We know that Eudoxus recoiled before the frank introduction of the irrational for metaphysical reasons—an *a priori* notion of existence which was limited to finite sets of integers. But science pushed ahead; it could not avoid this creation without the complications which the sixth book of Euclid (which is due to Eudoxus) shows so clearly. Once the number was introduced, the symbol $\sqrt{2}$ was adopted. The needs of science required inexorably the introduction of new elements, of new symbols. In order that the set of real numbers be *complete*, in the sense indicated by topology, transcendental numbers had to be introduced. Then, in order that this set be *compact*, two more numbers, designated by $+\infty$ and $-\infty$, were introduced. Now the set of *real numbers* was considered attained; all numbers introduced thereafter were no longer called *real*!

In geometry, the line was considered an element given globally and to be analyzed as a set of points; it is precisely this analysis that has enriched the concept of the real number. For us, today, the real line is defined as a set consisting of its points, and it serves as a model for the set of real numbers—it therefore has two points which correspond, respectively, to $+\infty$ and $-\infty$.

But in projective geometry, we consider that these two points on the line define only *one* element at infinity, called the *point at infinity*; then a plane has "one line at infinity." In the geometry of inversion (or anallagmatic geometry), space is considered to have a single point at infinity, this point being common to all lines and to all planes. In algebraic geometry, we define imaginary points, lines, and planes as corresponding to imaginary (or complex) numbers.

Thus even in the field of elementary mathematics examples of extension abound. We shall return to this essential notion in the next chapter.

V

Today the angel Topology and the demon Abstract Algebra struggle for the soul of each of the mathematical domains.

—HERMANN WEYL

A FEW STEPS
IN THE NEW MATHEMATICS

Modern mathematics rests on the substructure of *mathematical logic* and the *theory of sets,* as we have seen. Upon this base rise the two pillars that support the whole edifice: *general algebra* and *general topology.* We use the word "general" in the same sense as does the naturalist when he distinguishes between general botany, which studies the structures and functions of the organs of plants, and specialized botany which identifies them in each specifically described species and family. In the same way we distinguish between general geography and the monographs that are written about specific countries and specific rivers. We are, then, talking about abstract and formal theories that can be applied to different objects (points, numbers, functions, geometric transformations, etc.). We have noted that by forcing the language we can sometimes use the same word for quite different things in theories which are isomorphic, and, generally, in different models of the same theory. It is, however, necessary to create words and symbols adapted to the exposition of an abstract theory which can then be translated into the special vocabulary of different models. We cannot imitate the infant who says "Daddy" to any man whatever, or the man who, if he is a Parisian, uses "Seine" as the name for every river!

The search for an axiomatic exposition necessarily requires several stages. The first is a survey of the kind that a naturalist makes. In Lebesgue's words: "The mathematician must explore the terrain in which he works, observe the mathematical entities he finds there, watch them living, so to speak, in order that he may discern their qualities and recognize the significance of these qualities." The outcome of this survey is the recognition of mathematical structures. Historical research is of great value at this stage, because the various structures were not all introduced simultaneously and history is in a sense an experience to be deciphered. The second stage is the experimental work. As Dieudonné puts it, we now study these structures in "pure cultures." At this point our exposition proceeds in the manner of the *Elements* of Bourbaki. Finally, there is the systematic study of the regions in which these structures reign.

To begin with, let us sketch the first stage briefly and show how a special vocabulary permits us to abstract general ideas from the specific cases in which they are observed—a tedious job which has been especially pursued since Vieta but which time constantly outmodes (as we can see by so many ambiguous and defective expressions: square, cube, tangent of an angle, etc.). In algebra the structures appear particularly clean-cut because their formalism was introduced early; therefore the work in this area, if it remains superficial, may seem useless and a little pedantic; it usually consists of no more than a listing of the definition of words. Since we cannot make a careful and constructive study, we shall cover abstract algebra rather quickly; topology will be more interesting, for there the useful structures are more hidden and are indistinct to the eyes of the profane, who have only a global and intuitive notion of topological questions.

General Algebra

Since we are going to think in terms of sets, let us start with the fundamental concept of *mapping* a set *into* another (or *upon* another, a distinction which we shall make more precise).

Let E and F be two sets; a mapping of E *into* F is a law whereby we associate an element x of E with *one and only one* element y of F. We write, $y = f(x)$. We say that this law is a function of x, E being the *starting set* (the *domain*) and F the *finishing set* (the *range*). We say also that the function f is *defined* in E and *takes its values* in F. But it may happen that the function is defined only for elements which form a subset A of E: then we say that the function is defined *upon* A; the set of images constitutes a subset B of F and we write, B = f(A) (by an abuse of notation) to mean:

$$\forall x, x \in A \Rightarrow f(x) \in B$$

and $$\forall y, y \in B \Rightarrow \exists x, y = f(x)$$

(We recall that "$\forall x$" is read "for any x" and that "$\exists x$" is read, "there exists at least one x such that.") A mapping of E *upon* F is such that every element of F is reached; that is, f(B) = F.

On the other hand, if we consider two sets, E and F, we can construct a new set G by taking, as constituent elements of G, *ordered pairs*, of which the first term a is an element of E, and of which the second term b is an element of F. Such an ordered pair is designated by (a, b) in which a is the *generating element* of E and b is the generating element of F, if we call a generating element of a set any element of the set which can be replaced by every element of the set (this corresponds to the variable point with variable coordinates in analytic geometry). The set of ordered pairs G is called the *cartesian product* of E and F, and is symbolized by G = E $\times$ F (read, "E cross F").

Here is an illustration of a cartesian product. Let E be the set of points in a plane and let F be the set of real numbers. G then will be the set of points in the space defined in numerical geometry, E being the set of projections and F the set of values. In abstract algebra, E and F are called the *factors* of the cartesian product, E being the first projection (component) of G, and F being the second projection (component) of G.

Internal Laws of Composition

Suppose now that we let E and F be the same set E and consider the ordered pairs that form the cartesian product $\varepsilon = E \times E$. One of the principal aims of algebra is to study the mappings of ε into E.

Example 1. Let E be the set of integers. To each ordered pair (x, y) we associate an integer u, called the *sum* of x and y, by the operation called *addition*. In symbols: $x + y = u$.

Example 2. In the set E of rational numbers, associate to each ordered pair (x, y) the rational number $u = xy$, called the product of x and y.

Example 3. In the set of translations E, associate to each ordered pair (x, y) a translation which is obtained by applying the translation x to every figure F, and then, to the resulting figure F', the translation y which results in F''. We can then indicate the combined translation as $xy = u$; this transforms F into F''.

Example 4. The same is true if E is the set of rotations and translations in a plane. (We must include rotations *and* translations, because the resultant of two rotations is not always a rotation; it may be a translation.)

Example 5. Let E be the set of vectors that used to be called "free" vectors (to distinguish them from slide or axial vectors). Associate to each ordered pair (a, b) of two vectors the vector called the vector product, which is designated by $x \times y = u$.

Example 6. Let E be the set of positive integers. To the ordered pair (x, y) associate the integer $x^y = u$.

Example 7. Let E be the set of subsets of a set A. To the ordered pair (x, y) of two subsets of A we associate another subset:

$$\text{(a) The union, } x \cup y = u$$

or $\qquad\qquad$ (b) The intersection, $x \cap y = u$

Example 8. Let E be the set of positive integers. To each ordered pair (x, y) associate:

$$\text{(a) The lowest common multiple of } x \text{ and } y$$

$$\text{(b) The greatest common factor of } x \text{ and } y$$

All these operations are called *internal laws of composition of E,* for each component of the ordered pair belongs to E, and the image obtained also belongs to E. (As a counter-example, the multiplication of a vector by a number to obtain a vector, or the scalar product of two vectors which gives a number, is not an internal operation within the set of vectors.) Moreover, these operations are binary, since the domain is the set of ordered pairs, and the two components of each ordered pair are the "terms of the operation."

What observations can we make on these operations, and what questions will give us a principle of classification? In a general way, let us agree to indicate any such operation by:

$$x \circ y = u$$

which is read, "x operating on y equals u."

Commutativity. Do we have, $\forall x$, $\forall y$, $x \circ y = y \circ x$? The answer is "yes" for examples 1, 2, 3, 7 and 8, and "no" for the others.

Are there neutral elements, e, such that:

$$\forall x, \; x \circ e = e \circ x = x?$$

In example 1, there is one such element, 0, if we consider 0 an integer, but there is *none* if we consider only the positive integers. In example 2, the element is the number 1 (unity). In example 3, it is the translation of the null-vector, if we accept it as a translation under the name of the identical translation. The same holds for example 4. There is no neutral element in example 5 or example 6, since $x^1 = x$ but $1^x \neq x$. In example 7, there is the empty set for (a) and the set E itself for (b). In example 8(a), it is the number 1, but there is none in example 8(b).

Is cancellation possible from the left, that is, is it true that:

$$(x \circ y = x \circ y') \Leftrightarrow (y = y')?$$

or from the right, that is, is it true that:

$$(x \circ y = x' \circ y) \Leftrightarrow (x = x')?$$

The two concepts become one if the operation is commutative. The answer is "yes" for examples 1, 3, 4 and 6 (because we are thinking of positive numbers, it would be "no" with signed integers).

The answer is "no" for examples 5, 7 and 8. In example 2, it would be "yes" if we exclude the number 0 from the set under consideration; we say here that 0 is not *regular*.

Are there idempotent elements; that is, does $x \circ x = x$?

Obviously the neutral element, if there is one, satisfies this requirement; there are no others if the operations are simplifiable, because then:

$$x \circ x = x \circ e \Rightarrow x = e$$

In example 6, where we admit the set of negative numbers, the number -1 is idempotent without being a neutral element. In examples 7 and 8 all the elements are idempotent.

Are there symmetrical elements x' so that $x \circ x' = e$ in the cases in which neutral elements exist?

If we consider the set of signed integers in example 1, each has a symmetrical element (*e.g.*, $+3$ and -3). They are called *opposites*, because the operation is named *addition* (or *additive inverses*). In example 2, all elements except 0 have a symmetrical element which is called an *inverse*, because the operation is called multiplication (*e.g.*, 3/4 and 4/3).

Associativity. Finally, if the operation is defined for all ordered pairs of E, it can be repeated:

$$x \circ y = u, \quad u \circ z = v$$

which can be written as:

$$(x \circ y) \circ z = v$$

Is it then true that:

$$(x \circ y) \circ z = x \circ (y \circ z)?$$

The operations are associative in all our examples with the exception of 5 and 6.

We will stop our list of questions at this point; we have seen that even though a set is provided with only one operation, that operation can be subjected to a variety of axioms. In this way a great variety of structures can be obtained; it is necessary to determine what are the consistent and independent axioms, and to draw consequences from them.

Among the many different structures that can be imposed upon a set provided with only one operation, the most important is that of a *group*. A set upon which one internal operation is defined is said to have the structure of a group if

(1) the operation is associative;
(2) there exists a neutral element;
(3) each element has a symmetrical element.

If, moreover, the operation is commutative, the group is said to be Abelian (after the Norwegian mathematician, Abel).

What can be simpler than such a definition, and what kind of building can be erected on so infantile a foundation? Certainly it needs no great erudition—no, nothing more than genius! In fact, it was two children who did it, two children of marvelous genius: Niels Henrik Abel (1802–1829) whose first work was a proof of the impossibility of the algebraic solution of the general equation of the fifth degree, and whose works in analysis "left the world enough work to do for 500 years"; and Evariste Galois (1811–1832) who, during the tragic night of his death on May 29, 1832, summarized feverishly his theory of groups, a theory which determines under what conditions an equation of any degree can be solved in terms of radicals.

Galois groups can be related to polynomials by considering not the roots defined by different expressions for each of them but the roots defined by the set of all of them. This work was continued by Camille Jordan. Lebesgue described his contributions as follows: "[He] utilized the happy method of Galois, whose essential point is the introduction of a certain group of substitutions, already perceived by Lagrange, which could be attached to every algebraic equation and in which the properties of the equation would be reflected faithfully. But to know how to look into this mirror, one has to have learned to distinguish between the various qualities of groups of substitutions and to have reasoned about them. . . . Thus the properties of equations are derived from the proportion of groups of substitutions. . . . The study of the groups of algebraic equations encountered in the greatest variety of equations lead to conclusions that certain relations exist, relations unsuspected until then, somewhat in the manner in which the comparison of dimensional equations suggests relations between physical magnitudes."

Thus we meet groups in a variety of theories. If we look back to the examples given above, we see that example 1 defines the additive group of positive and negative integers (the set of positive integers is not an additive group). Example 2 defines the multiplicative group of the set obtained by eliminating 0 from the set E of the rational numbers. Examples 3 and 4 define the group of translations and the group of displacements in the plane, respectively; we note that these groups are multiplicative. The other examples do not define groups.

Let us now consider examples of groups of order n; that is, groups having n elements.

Take the three letters a, b and c, given at first in that order. A *substitution* is an operation which consists of changing the places of these letters; for three letters there are, therefore, six possible substitutions; they are the operations whereby we pass from the original arrangement (a, b, c) to:

$$(a, b, c)$$

$$(a, c, b)$$

$$(b, a, c)$$

$$(b, c, a)$$

$$(c, a, b)$$

$$(c, b, a)$$

Upon this set of six elements (the various substitutions) we define an operation called *product*. For example, for:

$$s_1 \begin{cases} a \rightsquigarrow b \\ b \rightsquigarrow a \\ c \rightsquigarrow c \end{cases} \text{ and } s_2 \begin{cases} a \rightsquigarrow c \\ b \rightsquigarrow a \\ c \rightsquigarrow b \end{cases}$$

we will write:

$$p = s_1 \times s_2 = \begin{cases} a \rightsquigarrow a \\ b \rightsquigarrow c \\ c \rightsquigarrow b \end{cases}$$

which is to say that the images by means of p are the images by means of s_2 of the images by means of s_1. A model of this is furnished by placing the three letters at the vertices of an equilateral triangle: the substitutions, then, are the two rotations through $+120°$ and $-120°$ about the center 0, and the three symmetries about the axes of the triangle (it is necessary, however, to add the identical transformation).

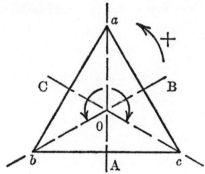

This geometric model permits us to classify the substitutions. We will call the identity transformation i, the rotation through $+120°$ r, and the rotation through $-120°$ r'. A, B, C are the three symmetries.

Let us exhibit the table of the operations which we have called multiplication:

		first factor					
		i	r	r'	A	B	C
	i	i	r	r'	A	B	C
	r	r	r'	i	C	A	B
second	r'	r'	i	r	B	C	A
factor	A	A	B	C	i	r	r'
	B	B	C	A	r'	i	r
	C	C	A	B	r	r'	i

$$p = \text{first factor} \times \text{second factor}$$

For example:

$$A \times r = C$$

because
$$\begin{bmatrix} a \smile a \smile b \\ b \smile c \smile a \\ c \smile b \smile c \end{bmatrix}$$

Similarly:

$$A \times r' = B$$

because
$$\begin{bmatrix} a \smile a \smile c \\ b \smile c \smile b \\ c \smile b \smile a \end{bmatrix}$$

This table shows that the set of six elements does indeed have the structure of a group. The i is the neutral element; since i occurs in each row and in each column, every element has a symmetrical element; and associativity is a consequence of the very definition of the substitutions. Moreover, we note that the operation is not commutative.

There are three subgroups of two elements each: (i, A), (i, B) and (i, C); and one subgroup of three elements: (i, r, r'). These four new groups have the peculiar property of being generated by a single element other than the neutral element. For the groups consisting of two elements, for example, we have, $A \times A = i$; for the group of three elements, we have:

$$r \times r = r'$$

$$r \times r \times r = i$$

and similarly:

$$r' \times r' = r$$

$$r' \times r' \times r' = i$$

A group of finite order which has these properties is called a *cyclic group*; the group consisting of six elements that we have defined is not a cyclic group. We can see that in a finite group every element generates a cyclic subgroup, which is the group itself, if the group is cyclic.

Just as the group we have been considering has as a model the symmetries and rotations that leave an equilateral triangle invariant, so we can imagine that the theory of groups would clarify the symmetries of regular polygons and regular polyhedrons. But the importance of groups becomes even more general when we consider them in connection with other structures.

Composite Structures: Rings and Fields

Suppose now that the set E which we have been studying is provided with two internal operations designated by, say, o and *; the two structures so determined by the properties of these operations will, in general, have relations between them, so that it becomes necessary to consider a *composite structure*. The most interesting connection between them is that of *distributivity*. The operation * is said to be distributive with respect to the operation o if for all elements of the set

$$a * (b \text{ o } c) = (a * b) \text{ o } (a * c)$$

and

$$(b \text{ o } c) * a = (b * a) \text{ o } (c * a)$$

These conditions become but one condition if the operation * is commutative. It is customary to designate a commutative operation *additively*, and a non-commutative operation *multiplicatively*.

If they are both commutative and if only one is distributive with respect to the other, the non-distributive element is designated *additively* and the distributive element *multiplicatively*. Such is the convention for the well-known instance of the system of real numbers.

We are now ready to define a very important structure: the structure of the *ring*.

A set E is provided with the *structure of a ring* if there are two internal operations defined for every ordered pair of elements and if they have the following three properties:

(1) E has the structure of an Abelian group for one of the operations. (This operation, therefore, we designate additively.)

(2) The second operation (designated multiplicatively) is associative.

(3) The second operation is distributive with respect to the first. If, moreover, the second operation is commutative, the ring is said to be commutative.

The most obvious illustration of a ring is the set of positive and negative integers. Another example is that of polynomials: It is precisely because the set of polynomials forms a ring that there are so many resemblances between the theory of polynomials and that of integers, especially if we restrict ourselves to polynomials with one variable.

Other rings of special importance in arithmetic are those formed by classes of integers which give the same remainder when they are divided by a divisor d chosen once for all: they are called *residue classes modulo d*.

For example, let $d = 3$. There are then three residue classes:

C_0 consisting of the numbers 0, 3, 6, $\cdots$, $3k$, $\cdots$, a, $\cdots$ where $a \equiv 0 \pmod 3$

C_1 consisting of the numbers 1, 4, 7, $\cdots$, $3k + 1$, $\cdots$, b, $\cdots$ where $b \equiv 1 \pmod 3$

C_2 consisting of the numbers 2, 5, 8, $\cdots$, $3k + 2$, $\cdots$, c, $\cdots$ where $c \equiv 2 \pmod 3$

We discover quickly that:

$$a + b \equiv 1, \qquad 2a \equiv 0, \qquad ab \equiv 0, \qquad a^2 \equiv 0$$

$$a + c \equiv 2, \qquad 2b \equiv 2, \qquad ac \equiv 0, \qquad b^2 \equiv 1$$

$$b + c \equiv 0, \qquad 2c \equiv 1, \qquad bc \equiv 2, \qquad c^2 \equiv 1$$

We can now operate on the classes themselves and arrive at the following tables of addition and multiplication:

+	C_0	C_1	C_2
C_0	C_0	C_1	C_2
C_1	C_1	C_2	C_0
C_2	C_2	C_0	C_1

×	C_0	C_1	C_2
C_0	C_0	C_0	C_0
C_1	C_0	C_1	C_2
C_2	C_0	C_2	C_1

We see that addition provides the set C_0, C_1, C_2 with the structure of an additive group which has the neutral element C_0 and which is commutative. The same is true for multiplication, the neutral element being C_1. We can check that the structure is distributive (it is sufficient to multiply on one side, since multiplication here is commutative).

We can state in the same way the example of the residue classes, modulo 4:

+	C_0	C_1	C_2	C_3
C_0	C_0	C_1	C_2	C_3
C_1	C_1	C_2	C_3	C_0
C_2	C_2	C_3	C_0	C_1
C_3	C_3	C_0	C_1	C_2

×	C_0	C_1	C_2	C_3
C_0	C_0	C_0	C_0	C_0
C_1	C_0	C_1	C_2	C_3
C_2	C_0	C_2	C_0	C_2
C_3	C_0	C_3	C_2	C_1

We can see that we still have the structure of a group: C_0 is still the neutral element for addition and C_1 is the neutral element for multiplication. But in the case of modulo 3, every element except C_0 has an inverse—that is, a symmetrical element with respect to multiplication—while in the case of modulo 4, C_2 does not have an inverse, because C_1 does not appear in the rows and columns that begin with C_2. A study of arithmetic shows that the fact that every element except C_0 has an inverse is associated with the fact that d is a prime number. The distinction is therefore an important one.

Let us make and retain a new distinction: A *ring* such that every element except the neutral element with respect to addition has a multiplicative inverse is called a *field*. We say that we have a *commutative field* if multiplication is also commutative.

The set of integers is a ring but not a field; it is, by extension, immersed in the field of rational numbers.

Rings of residue classes are fields if the modulus is a prime number.

Complex numbers also form a commutative field. They can be generated from the real numbers and a symbol i by using the usual formal rules of addition and multiplication and the additional rule $i^2 = -1$.

The field of complex numbers is commutative and multiplication is distributive with respect to addition. Complex numbers are of the form $a + ib$, where a and b are real. The ring defined in this way is a field, if we exclude $O + Oi$, because:

$$(a + ib) \cdot \left(\frac{a}{a^2 + b^2} - i \frac{b}{a^2 + b^2} \right) = 1 + Oi = 1$$

Quaternions are defined in an analogous manner. They form a non-commutative field. They are constructed by using the real numbers and the three symbols i, j and k by means of the multiplication table

$\times$	r	i	j	k
r	r^2	ri	rj	rk
i	ir	-1	$-k$	j
j	jr	k	-1	$-i$
k	kr	$-j$	i	-1

The quaternions are therefore of the form $a + bi + cj + dk$.

We can verify the fact that multiplication is distributive with respect to addition. The existence of the multiplicative inverse follows from the identity:

$$(a + bi + cj + dk) \cdot \left(\frac{a - ib - jc - kd}{a^2 + b^2 + c^2 + d^2}\right) = 1$$

Just as complex numbers can be interpreted as vectors in a two-dimensional space, so quaternions have a model in a vector space of four dimensions. Let us now give definitions of such spaces.

External Law of Composition: Vector Spaces

We understand what is meant by "multiplying a vector by a real number." It means that the direction of the vector is retained, and we multiply its length by the absolute value of the real number, then retain or change the sense of the vector according to whether the real number is positive or negative. By this process an operation is performed on the set of vectors by means of the elements of another set—the real numbers R—which is a field. Such an operation is said to be an *external law of composition*.

In the case of vectors, we also define an internal, commutative operation called *addition* (it used to be called "the geometric sum of two vectors"; now we merely call it "the sum of two vectors"). It is defined by the so-called "parallelogram" rule. The vector Ω of length zero (which we must accept as a vector) is the neutral element. Every vector has an inverse. In short, the set of vectors has the structure of an additive, commutative group.

Moreover, multiplication by a real number is distributive with respect to the addition of vectors. Multiplication of a vector by the sum of two real numbers also is distributive:

$$a(V + W) = aV + aW$$

and
$$(a + b)V = aV + bV$$

Finally, we have the property

$$a(bV) = (ab)V$$

and $OV = \Omega$

$$1V = V$$

Whenever we have any set of elements V and any field of elements consisting of elements a, b, $\cdots$, these properties characterize a *vector space*.

For example, consider the field of real numbers, R, and the set of trinomials $\alpha x^2 + \beta x + \gamma$, where α, β and γ are members of R. The set of such trinomials, with the ordinary rules of operation, constitutes a vector space. The base vectors are x^2, x and 1.

Further examples are provided by the set of continuous functions and the set of differentiable functions. This is what explains the use of the term "space" in an abstract sense. Thus the complex numbers form a vector space if we introduce a symbol e to represent the neutral element for multiplication. In our multiplication table, where we had the real number r we now write, $r{\cdot}e$; so that e and i become two independent signs considered as "vectors," and every complex number $x = ae + bi$ (a and b being real numbers) is a vector in a two-dimensional space. Similarly, the quaternions $x = ae + bi + cj + dk$ are vectors in a space of four dimensions.

In a vector space, a set of independent vectors (such as e, i, j, k) constitutes a *base*, and the other vectors are expressed with the help of this base as the sums of the products of the basic vectors and the real numbers, as we have just indicated for the vector x. We can prove that the *number* of basic vectors is completely determined for a vector space, whatever may be the chosen base—this number is the *dimension* of the vector space. The dimension may be finite or infinite. It is finite, and equal to three, for the set of trinomials (for we can choose the three "vectors" 1, x and x^2); but it is infinite for the set of continuous functions.

We are aware that elementary geometry is a study of point transformations (translations, rotations, symmetries of various kinds, homothecies, similitudes and inversions are the transformations most often considered). Since space itself appears to us as a vector space (the very idea of analytic geometry is the definition of a point M by means of the projections of the vector OM on the coordinate axes), point transformations appear as correspondences between vector spaces, which, in our examples, are superposed one upon the other. We are then talking about *the mapping of one vector space upon another*. We can think of some very complicated ones, but the simple ones are clearly those that preserve the addition of vectors (that is, the image of a sum of two vectors is the sum of the images) and that preserve, also, multiplication by the elements of the field R (if V′ is the image of V, kV′ is the image of kV). Under these conditions, if a base which is designated, as above, by e, i, j and k has for its image e', i', j' and k', then every vector $x = ae + bi + cj + dk$ has for its image $x' = ae' + bi' + cj' + dk'$. We then say that we have a *linear mapping of one vector space upon another*. This is simply the preservation of the coordinates: the transformation is determined if we are given the base and its image. If the two spaces are superimposed, one upon the other, the image of the base is given with respect to the base of the original space:

$$e' = \alpha_1 e + \beta_1 i + \gamma_1 j + \delta_1 k$$

$$i' = \alpha_2 e + \beta_2 i + \gamma_2 j + \delta_2 k$$

$$j' = \alpha_3 e + \beta_3 i + \gamma_3 j + \delta_3 k$$

$$k' = \alpha_4 e + \beta_4 i + \gamma_4 j + \delta_4 k$$

In other words, the transformation is characterized by a square array of numbers (in our example $4^2 = 16$ numbers):

$$
\begin{array}{cccc}
\alpha_1 & \beta_1 & \gamma_1 & \delta_1 \\
\alpha_2 & \beta_2 & \gamma_2 & \delta_2 \\
\alpha_3 & \beta_3 & \gamma_3 & \delta_3 \\
\alpha_4 & \beta_4 & \gamma_4 & \delta_4
\end{array}
$$

This array is called a *square matrix*. In considering the "products of linear mappings," we have to define the "product of matrices." Transformations such as a projection of space on a plane, which changes dimensions, lead to the introduction of non-square (*i.e.,* rectangular) matrices. Let us add that since all systems of linear equations can be interpreted as representing the intersection of planes in a vector space of a convenient number of dimensions, the theory of matrices rules in this domain, and numbers called "determinants" appear.

We have just given a flood of definitions; it should be understood that if we have introduced so many ideas and so many words, it is only because the already known mathematical theories have demonstrated their importance. If the same operational structure has appeared in many guises, it makes for a profound increase in comprehension to construct one abstract theory the study of which is applicable to all abstract theories.

Each of the preceding sections in this chapter is an introduction to the studies that constitute general algebra, in which many beautiful theorems have been discovered. If one particular model of a theory suggests a result, all the other models profit from it immediately. As an example we shall give one last definition.

Ideals

Some readers may have been struck by the use of the word "ideal" in mathematics. Can we get some idea of what it is? An *ideal* is a mathematical entity that appears in certain rings. To give the set E the structure of a ring, it is provided with an addition for which it is a group, and with a multiplication which is associative and which is distributive with respect to the addition. The best-known example is that of the integers. In the theory of integers appears the concept of prime numbers and the fundamental theorem of unique factorization, which states that every integer can be represented in one and only one way, as a product of prime numbers. In the most general rings the uniqueness of decomposition into prime factors no longer holds. Kummer (1810–1893) discovered that this uniqueness can be recaptured if the set E is immersed in a richer set F by the creation of new elements which he named "ideals."

In the set of integers, let a and b be two elements. The set α of numbers $n = ua + vb$, where u and v are any integers, has a great stability in E; the sum of two numbers of $\mathcal{A}$ also belongs to $\mathcal{A}$ and the product of a number $n \in \mathcal{A}$ by any element of E also belongs to $\mathcal{A}$. Now this set is very important for the ordered pair (a, b), because (as can be shown without difficulty) the smallest number of $\mathcal{A}$ is the greatest common divisor d of a and b, and all the numbers $n \in \mathcal{A}$ are multiples of d (including a and b and their common multiples). The set $\mathcal{A}$ is the *ideal* generated by a and b. But the set is also generated by the unique number d; we then call it a *principal* ideal; actually the set is not indispensable to the theory, for the number d represents it perfectly. (In particular, the set of integers is a principal ideal generated by the number 1; it is also generated by any two relatively prime numbers.)

Now let E be the set of polynomials in one variable x with integral coefficients. Let us consider the ideal generated by the ordered pair $(2, x)$, which is the set of polynomials $N = P(x) \times 2 + Q(x) \times x$. This set $\mathcal{A}$ satisfies the two stated conditions that constitute the definition of an ideal: the sum of two elements of the set $\mathcal{A}$ belongs to $\mathcal{A}$, as do their products by any polynomial which is an element of E. But this time the ideal cannot be generated by a unique element of E, not even by 1, because $3 + x$, for example, does not belong to $\mathcal{A}$. It is therefore not a principal ideal. If we find it useful for a theory to consider it as an element of our set, we will have to make an extension of E. Such considerations have taken on great importance in following up the work of Dedekind in algebra and in the theory of numbers, thanks to Emmy Noether in particular.

Relations

We cannot leave algebra without saying a word about the *relations* that superimpose themselves on the operations for characterizing structures.

When we gave the example of residue classes modulo the integer d, we considered as *equivalent* all integers which gave the same remainder when divided by d. The set of integers then was found to be divided into d equivalence classes. In general, an equivalence relation (sometimes designated by $\equiv$) is defined as a relation of two members having

(1) reflexivity: $\quad a \equiv a,$
(2) symmetry: $\quad [a \equiv b] \Leftrightarrow [b \equiv a],$
(3) transitivity: $\quad [a \equiv b \text{ and } b \equiv c] \Leftrightarrow [a \equiv c].$

This results in a "partition" of the set into equivalence classes.

Also well known are the *relations of strict order*, such as "less than," designated by $<$. They are defined by:

(1) non-reflexivity: $\quad a < a$ being false,
(2) non-symmetry: $\quad a < b$ and $b < a$ being mutually exclusive,
(3) transitivity: $\quad [a < b \text{ and } b < c] \Rightarrow [a < c].$

Non-strict relations of order, such as "not greater than" (written $\leq$), are defined by:

(1) reflexivity: $\quad a \leq a$ being true,
(2) anti-symmetry: $\quad [a \leq b \text{ and } b \leq a] \Rightarrow [a = b],$
(3) transitivity: $\quad [a \leq b \text{ and } b \leq c] \Rightarrow [a \leq c].$

In current language, the relation of strict order is translated by the words "before," "below," etc. In the ring of integers or of polynomials, the relation "being a divisor of" is a relation of order generally considered non-strict; this last example is one of sets not *totally ordered*, since all the elements are not comparable by the relation of order. The number 3 is a divisor of 6, but 3 and 7 are not divisors of each other. The same is true for polynomials: $x + 1$ and $x^2 - 1$ are comparable by the relation "is a divisor of," but $x + 1$ and $x + 2$ are not.

The relation of inclusion, written $\subset$ in the theory of sets, is a relation of order which is utilized in defining *lattice theory*.

General Topology

Let us take a piece of white paper. What study can we make of its points? Plane geometry, someone says. Certainly, but everything depends on what we mean by geometry. There is more to consider than triangles and parallelograms!

Under the name "analysis situs" or "topology" mathematicians have studied the problems of arrangements and relative positions of figures constructed on an elastic surface: problems such as counting the number of regions bounded by straight lines or by planes, or the famous formula of Euler, which connects the number of vertices, faces, and edges of any polyhedron by the formula $F + V - E = 2$. Such problems are often very difficult to solve even when they are easy to state (as is true in the theory of integers). For example, modern science has yet to solve the four-color map problem, which simply asks whether four colors are always sufficient for coloring the regions of a plane in such a way that any two regions having a common boundary are of different colors. Also, questions arise about connectivity on surfaces of different types, such as the plane, the sphere, the torus, and surfaces with any number of holes—questions which modern algebra has revived. Here we shall only introduce some of the primary notions of general topology.

On our piece of white paper let us spill a drop of red ink. All the points on the paper then are either red or white, it would seem. But now let us try to outline the spot with a black line. That is easy, if the spot is clear—just follow its boundary line. But is a line not a set of points? Before we draw the line, what color are its points? One might be tempted to say, red on one side, and white on the other—but clearly no meaningful answer is possible. The question is therefore badly stated.

When in elementary geometry we trace a circle with a given center O and a given radius R, we can distinguish not two but three sets of points: the set I composed of points i such that $Oi < R$, which constitutes the *interior region;* the set E of points e such that $Oe > R$ (the *exterior region*); the set C of points c such that $Oc = R$ (the *common boundary* of the interior and exterior regions).

The union of the interior and the boundary, $F - I \cup C$, is called a *closed set*, while I is an *open set* of points; the boundary C is the smallest set of points which, united with I, gives a closed set. Naturally, if we unite I with only a part of C, we get a set which is neither open nor closed.

What we have just said without precise definitions, if we replace the circle by a blot, corresponds to an intuitive topology of the plane. In particular cases we can define some *natural* topologies, which we shall take up later.

If the set of real numbers and its relation of order are known, we say that the set of x's defined by $a < x < b$ is an *open interval*, and $a \leq x \leq b$ is a *closed interval*. The boundary is constituted by the two points a and b. But in this topology we also call "open" every union of open intervals and every intersection of a finite number of open intervals. As for "closed intervals," they are the complements of open ones. (Complementation is defined in the preceding chapter.)

Similarly, in the plane of Euclidean metric geometry, a "natural" topology will be introduced by calling "open" any union of interiors of circles, as well as the intersections of a finite number of them; the closed ones are the complements of the open ones. In all cases, the open members of the set must be defined; these are the subsets which are subject to the conditions that we have already given twice.

O_1: any union of open sets is an open set.

O_2: any intersection of a finite number of open sets is an open set.

Any complement of an open set is called a closed set. Finally, we have to agree to consider the universal set and the null set as open and closed at the same time.

When any set A, included in E, has been given, we say that a point i is *interior* if there exists an open set containing i which is included in A; the set of these points i is *the interior* I of A; therefore I is included in A ($I \subset A$). *An open set is its own interior.*

As for the boundary C of A, it is the set of points c such that *all* open sets containing c have points in common with A, but also have points in common with the complement of A; such points c may or may not belong to A. If A is *open*, it does not contain any point of its boundary; if it is closed, all of its boundary points belong to it.

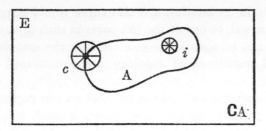

All this may seem very simple if we think of our ink blot on the sheet of paper, but even this introductory part of the study may become very delicate, as anyone knows who has heard about the curves that were invented precisely to underline these difficulties. For example, what could be simpler than the trajectory of a point in the plane whose coordinates x and y are continuous functions of time? And yet, Peano has given us an example of just such a curve which passes through every point in the interior of a square! Such a curve is certainly not a boundary. If, on the contrary, we wish to consider a curve which *is* a boundary, Kerékjártó gives us one which is the common frontier of *three* regions, and each point of which is a boundary point for all three regions! Let us not rush into confusing "boundary" with "curve!"

If, in the set E, we have defined the open subsets that satisfy the given axioms, we say that E has become a *topological space:* a topology has been defined upon it. From this we get a very important concept: if a is any point of E, a *neighborhood* of this point is *any set which contains an open subset that contains this point.* Naturally the "small" neighborhoods are the most interesting; in what follows, for the sake of simplicity, we will consider only open neighborhoods. (On the line, we will take small open intervals containing the point, and in the Euclidean metric plane, small squares or small disks that contain the point.) It is clear that an open set is a neighborhood of every one of its points, since all its points are *interior*. This property characterizes open sets.

Let us give one more definition: A set A is said to be *connected* if it is possible to partition it into two "disjoint" open sets, that is, "without common points." (This corresponds to the notion of a domain with only one tenant: if we wish to partition it, we must trace a curve in its interior, and this curve would have to belong, at least piecemeal, to one of the two parts in such a way that these parts could not be open.) We now see how the questions of connectivity of combinatorial topology are encountered in general topology.

Let us now suppose that the red blot on our paper is an open set, and let us place on one of its points a small insect. We can modernize the paradox of Achilles and the tortoise and say that the insect cannot leave the blot. In effect, whenever it is on the blot it is on the inside of an open set, and it cannot reach the boundary, being always imprisoned in an open set.

With these prison-neighborhoods, let us set some traps. We shall permit the insect to go to a point a in the open set but forbid it to approach a point b; thus we are considering a neighborhood $N(a)$ and a neighborhood $N(b)$ of each of these two points, and we stipulate that these neighborhoods be disjoint. The possibility of defining such neighborhoods for any two points a and b, of separating them in this way, characterizes a *Hausdorff topological space*.

When this proposed condition has been realized, let us be more and more cruel to the poor creature. We now bar it from the neighborhoods of points b of $N(a)$, of b_1 of $N_1(a)$, etc. Its prison becomes more and more confining as the neighborhoods of a becomes smaller and smaller:

$$N(a) \supset N_1(a) \supset N_2(a) \supset \cdots \supset N_n(a) \supset \cdots$$

We say that the set of these neighborhoods constitutes a particular *filter base,* called the *system of neighborhoods of a.* This is only a very special case, because we have always retained the point a, but we do not pretend to define in its complete generality either a *filter base* or a *filter*. Let us say only that the *filter of neighborhoods* of a would be the set of all the subsets that contain the neighborhoods of a, and that in very general spaces the filters occur as generalizations of the notion of sequences, this notion being specially usable in metric spaces (as we shall see later).

Let us continue indefinitely to exclude the neighborhoods of the points $b, b_1, \cdots$. Perhaps we do not thus remove all points other than a, since each neighborhood of a can have a non-denumerable number of points, but why not continue transfinitely? All the points save a are then excluded in the limit, and we say that the *filter converges toward* a.

Other filters can converge toward a curve, or toward a subset, or not converge at all, but for a filter of neighborhoods of a point the condition of "separability" assures the uniqueness of the limit point.

On separable topological spaces we easily define the *continuity of a function*. Let X and Y be two separable spaces, and let $y = f(x)$ be a function which defines a mapping of X into Y. Let there be a point a of X and a point $b = f(a)$, its image in Y. There is continuity at the point a if, however small a neighborhood $W(b)$ in Y is chosen, the condition $y \in W(b)$ is assured if we impose on x the condition that it be in a sufficiently small neighborhood $N(a)$ of a in X. In a precise fashion, the function is continuous at the point a if, whatever neighborhood $W(b)$ is chosen, there exists a neighborhood $N(a)$ such that $x \in N(a)$ assures that $y \in W(b)$. This is written:

$$\forall W(b), \ \exists N(a) : [x \in N(a)] \Rightarrow [y \in W(b)]$$

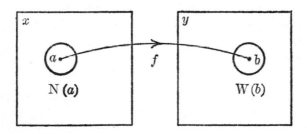

Since $W(b)$ may be reduced as much as we please, we see that the condition could also be stated as: "Any filter base that converges toward a has as an image a filter base which converges toward b."

This manner of definition by means of sets suggests the application of the notion of continuity to very diverse functions which barely resemble the numerical functions for which X and Y are both the field of real numbers. Once we accept the complex numbers, the question is no longer the same; now we consider functions for which X is a set of lines or even a set of functions and Y also can stop being a set of numbers. We see therefore that continuity is defined if we have defined a topology on the abstract spaces considered.

Thus in order to pass from numerical functions to general analysis, we have had to examine the reasons for the success of the demonstrations organized by Cauchy and to isolate the properties of sets which our intuition perceives in an apparently inextricable mixture.

On our sheet of paper it is often useful to place a grid over the region that contains a domain whose form or area, for example, we wish to ascertain approximately; in order not to omit points, we use squares with their boundaries, which gives a *covering with closed sets*. But it is preferable to utilize open domains that overlap, as on road maps, on which some localities are on the interior of two neighboring maps. We thus obtain a *covering with open sets* for the region A.

Certain discussions on continuity or on the definition of integrals require a condition called the *condition of compactness*. A topological space is said to be *compact* if all coverings with open sets contain a covering with a finite number of open sets. This is called the axiom of Borel-Lebesgue. Such spaces have simpler properties than non-compact spaces; but it is often sufficient for applications that every point of a separable set have a *compact neighborhood;* we say then that the space is *locally* compact. For example, the real straight line is not compact, but all the segments of the line are compact, so that the straight line is locally compact. If we adjoin to a straight line a point at infinity, it becomes closed and compact (special case of a theorem of Alexandroff's). Many theorems can be demonstrated; we transcribe the statements of some of these to show the spirit of the theory:

In a separable space, the union of two compact sets is compact.
The cross-product of compact sets is compact.
If f is a continuous mapping of a compact space X on a separable space Y, the image $f(X)$ is compact in Y.

Up to now we have been talking about what we call topologies. But we can define another type of structure which is of great importance—the *uniform structure*. It consists of giving a precise meaning to an intuitive notion: "two points are neighbors and there are other points which are neighbors of the two neighboring points." We will give an example. We consider the vector space $x = au + bv$, de-

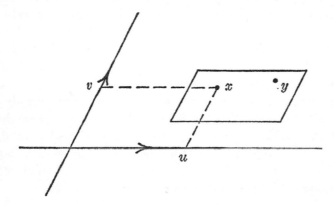

fined with the aid of the base u, v; in other words, we make an affine geometry. We say that "two points x and y are neighbors of order α" if they are in the same parallelogram whose sides, parallel to u and v respectively, are less than αu and αv. We will write this symbolically:

$$x \, N_\alpha y$$

This relation satisfies the three properties which are the axioms of the theory of uniform structures:

(1) reflexivity: $x \, N_\alpha x$ is true for every x and α
(2) symmetry: $x \, N_\alpha y \Leftrightarrow y \, N_\alpha x$
(3) $\forall \alpha$, $\exists \alpha_1$ such that $[x \, N_{\alpha_1} x_1 \text{ and } x_1 \, N_{\alpha_1} x'] \Rightarrow [x \, N_\alpha x']$

Let us emphasize the essential fact that α_1 depends on α but not on x. In our example it is sufficient to take $\alpha_1 < 1/2 \, \alpha$. We can then speak of the set of parallelograms N_α from which we derive a set of parallelograms N_{α_1}, then a set of parallelograms N_{α_2}, etc. In continuing thus, the sides $\alpha_n u$ and $\alpha_n v$ tend toward zero, and any two chosen distinct points x and y always end up by "not being close

enough." The uniform structure is called separable when it is so for
the space considered, which we shall assume in what follows.

Let us now consider the rest of the subsets N_α, N_{α_1}, N_{α_2}, $\cdots$,
N_{α_n}, $\cdots$, such that each is included in the one that precedes:

$$N_\alpha \supset N_{\alpha_1} \supset N_{\alpha_2} \supset \cdots \supset N_{\alpha_n} \supset \cdots$$

and let us suppose that α_n tends toward zero; we obtain a Cauchy
sequence. Since the structure is separable, this sequence cannot tend
toward more than one point. But does it always tend toward a point?
Not always. If all the Cauchy sequences (or rather all the Cauchy
filters) tend toward a point, the space is called *complete*; and if it is
not complete, we invent points to complete it!

For example, in the vector space $x = au + bv$, already considered, let us suppose that the field in which a, b, and α are defined
is the field of rational numbers. All that we have said is valid, but
the space is not complete. Let us draw the parallelogram with diagonal
$p = au + bv$, $q = a'u + b'v$ (a, b, a' and b' are rational numbers) and
let us arrange these points in such a way that we have:

$$a^2 < 2, \quad b^2 < 3, \quad a'^2 > 2, \quad b'^2 > 3$$

Let us make $a' - a$ and $b' - b$ tend toward zero. The Cauchy
filter will not tend toward a point but, by *completion*, we create the
new number $\sqrt{2}$ in the set of a's and the new number $\sqrt{3}$ in the set
of b's; then the Cauchy filter will converge toward the point:

$$x = \sqrt{2}\, u + \sqrt{3}\, v \text{ of the completed space}$$

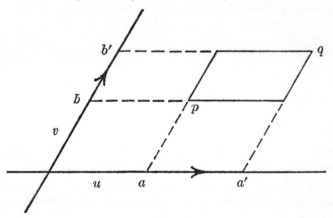

It should be noted that up to now we have not spoken of the *distance* between two points. That is why we have taken as an example the affine geometry in which the vectors *u* and *v* are not comparable. We know that the two-dimensional space of *metric* Euclidean geometry is obtained by defining what we mean by the vectors *u* and *v* being "*equal*" without being parallel, and by defining the "*right angle*" formed by these vectors. The base *u*, *v* is called orthogonal and it serves to create the analytical geometry of Descartes in which the distance between two points $x = au + bv$, $x' = a'u + b'v$ is obtained, by means of the Pythagorean theorem, by the formula:

$$d(x, x') = \sqrt{(a - a')^2 + (b - b')^2}$$

For an abstract space, we define a *metric space* in a general way by defining the *distance* between any two points (x, y). A distance is a *number* d *which is positive or zero* and which satisfies the axioms:

(1) $d(x, x) = 0$

(2) $d(x, y) = d(y, x)$

(3) $d(x, y) + d(y, z) \leqq d(x, z)$ (triangle inequality)

(4) $d(x, y) = 0$ whenever x and y are coincident

If condition (4) is not satisfied, we say we have defined not a distance but an *écart*, or pseudo distance.

For example, the Pythagorean formula written above defines a distance if a, a', b, b' range over the field of rational numbers, or even of real numbers, but it defines only an écart if these numbers range over the field of complex numbers, for then we can have $b - b' = i(a - a')$, whence $d(x, x') = 0$ even for distinct points (such points are located on the same isotropic line of the plane).

Upon every metric space we can define a topology associated with this metric: an *open neighborhood* of a point x will be the set of points x' satisfying $d(x, x') < R$, where R is a chosen positive number; this neighborhood is called an *open ball*. If we consider the metric space constituted by the Euclidean plane, the open ball is a disk.

With this metric is also associated a structure of a uniform space, because we can set:

$$[x \, N_\alpha x'] \Rightarrow [d(x, x') < \alpha]$$

which satisfies the required axioms.

Another example: Let us define, in two different ways, a distance in the set of continuous functions of one real variable, defined for the interval $0 \leqq x \leqq 1$:

(1)　　　　　　$d(f, g) = \text{maximum of } |f(x) - g(x)|$

(2)　　　　　　$\delta(f, g) = \int_0^1 |f(x) - g(x)| \, \mathrm{d}x$

We can easily verify that d and δ satisfy the properties that define a distance. They do not induce the same topology on the set of functions considered.

Composite Algebraico-Topological Structures

Now that we have indicated the principal algebraic and topological structures in such a way that we can imagine what a study of them in a "pure culture" would be, we must say a few words about the way in which they may be combined. Of course we have already touched on this in our examples, since we have utilized a uniform vector space and a metric vector space, with the associated topology and uniform structure.

We are going to take as an example the field of rational numbers and provide it with various topological structures.*

1. The *natural distance* of two elements r and r' of the field Q of rational numbers is

$$d(r, r') = |r - r'|$$

It is the absolute value (a positive number) of the difference between the two numbers. We can easily verify that it obeys the three axioms of distances:

* This study is somewhat technical, and the reader may wish to limit himself to reading the conclusions alone.

(a) $$d(r, r') = 0 \Leftrightarrow r = r'$$

(b) $$d(r, r') = d(r', r)$$

(c) $$d(r, r') + d(r', r'') \leqq d(r, r'')$$

The field of rational numbers is thus provided with the ordinary metric, called *Archimedian* because for any $r_0 \neq 0$ of absolute value $|r_0|$, and for any r_1 there exists an integer k such that $k|r_0|$ is greater than r_1 in absolute value.

To this metric correspond, as we have said, a topology and a uniform structure: two numbers r and r' are neighbors of order ϵ if $d(r, r')$ is less than ϵ:

$$r \, N_\epsilon r' \Leftrightarrow [d(r, r') < \epsilon] \Leftrightarrow [|r' - r| < \epsilon]$$

2. Let us consider only the field of rational, non-zero numbers Q^+. Let us introduce another uniform structure by the convention "r and r' are neighbors of order ϵ'," written, $r \, W_{\epsilon'} r'$ in the following sense:

$$r \, W_{\epsilon'} r' \Leftrightarrow \left[1 - \epsilon' < \frac{r}{r'} < 1 + \epsilon' \quad \text{and} \quad 1 - \epsilon' < \frac{r'}{r} < 1 + \epsilon' \right]$$

We take $\epsilon' < 1$ because the only interesting case is that in which the elements are "very close."

We must first verify that the axioms of a uniform structure are satisfied:

$r \, W_{\epsilon'} r$ is obviously true for any ϵ'.

The relation is certainly symmetrical for r and r'.

Finally, we must show that we can find an ϵ'_1 depending only on ϵ' and such that $r \, W_{\epsilon'} r'$ results from the system:

$$1 - \epsilon'_1 < \frac{r}{r_1} < 1 + \epsilon'_1 \qquad 1 - \epsilon'_1 < \frac{r_1}{r'} < 1 + \epsilon'_1$$

$$1 - \epsilon'_1 < \frac{r_1}{r} < 1 + \epsilon'_1 \qquad 1 - \epsilon'_1 < \frac{r'}{r_1} < 1 + \epsilon'_1$$

We find without difficulty that it is sufficient to take:

$$1 - \sqrt{1 - \epsilon'} < \epsilon'_1 < \sqrt{1 + \epsilon'} - 1$$

3. Let us return to the Archimedian distance $d(r, r') = |r - r'|$, introduced in the field of the rational positive and negative numbers. It has some properties that we have not noticed.

First, it defines the distance from the number r to the number 0 by $d(0, r) = |r|$. It is what we call the *norm* of the element of the field (here the norm of the element is equal to its absolute value). The field is thus *normalized* by the metric in question. The triangle inequality then gives us:

$$|r + r'| \leq |r| + |r'|$$

moreover,
$$|r \cdot r'| = |r| \cdot |r'|$$

In other words, the norm is *compatible with the multiplication* defined in the field.

All this said, we will now define, on the same field of rational numbers, a very different distance—a strange one that shocks common sense. The strangest thing about it is not that it exists but that it has such remarkable properties which are so important in arithmetic. It is the *p-adic distance*.

Let a prime number p (different from 1) be chosen once and for all. It is in reference to this number that the following definitions are constructed.

Let r be a rational number and a/b one of the fractions that represent this number. Let us exhibit the highest power of p in a and b:

$$a = p^{\alpha} a_1, \quad b = p^{\beta} b_1$$

where a_1 and b_1 are relatively prime to p and α and β may be zero.

We then have
$$r = p^n \frac{a_1}{b_1}, \quad n = \alpha - \beta$$

Let us notice that if we replace a/b by any other equivalent fraction, the number n does not change, since the same number is added to the exponents α and β. Therefore an integer, positive, negative or zero, is associated with the rational number r itself. It is called the *p-adic order of r.*

Let h be any positive number greater than 1. To the rational number r we associate the number h^{-n}, and we write:

$$|r|_p = h^{-n}$$

(and by convention $|0|_p = 0$).

We will show that it is a *norm*, that is, a *distance from the origin*. For if $r \neq 0$, it is a positive number. Then let $r = a/b$ and $r' = a'/b'$ be two rational numbers.

$$a = p^\alpha a_1 \qquad\qquad a' = p^{\alpha'} a_1'$$

$$b = p^\beta b_1 \qquad\qquad b' = p^{\beta'} b_1'$$

$$n = \alpha - \beta \qquad\qquad n' = \alpha' - \beta'$$

The absolute value (in the usual sense) of the sum of two numbers is:

$$|r + r'| = \frac{|ab' + ba'|}{|bb'|}$$

and
$$ab' + ba' = p^{\beta + \beta' + n} a_1 b_1' + p^{\beta + \beta' + n'} a_1' b_1$$

$$bb' = p^{\beta + \beta'} b_1 b_1'$$

Let us designate by Min (n, n') the *smaller* of the numbers n and n'; it is the p-adic order of $r + r'$, and consequently the p-adic norm of $r + r'$ is the *greater* of the p-adic norms of r and r':

$$|r + r'|_p = \text{Max} \,(|r|_p, \, |r'|_p)$$

This inequality is much stronger than the imposed inequality:

$$|r + r'|_p \leqq |r|_p + |r'|_p$$

In agreement with this p-adic norm, we easily define the *p-adic distance* of two rational numbers r and r' as the norm of $r - r'$:

$$d_p(r, r') = |r - r'|_p$$

and the triangle inequality is satisfied:

$$d_p(r, r'') = |(r'' - r') + (r' - r)|_p$$

$$= \text{Max}\,[d_p(r, r'), d_p(r', r'')]$$

$$\leq d_p(r, r') + d_p(r', r'')$$

We also set $\quad d_p(r, r) = 0$

To this p-adic metric corresponds an associated topology and we can define p-adic neighborhoods of order e by:

$$d_p(r, a) < e$$

however small e may be in the field of rational numbers. From this there results an associated uniform structure: two points are neighbors of order e if $d_p(r, r') < e$. From this we deduce the existence of Cauchy sequences as for the ordinary metric, and from this the possibility of *completing* the rational numbers by creating *p-adic non-rational numbers* just as we created the irrational numbers. Thus the set of rationals is immersed in two complete sets, *the set of real numbers* and the *p-adic numbers*.

The *p-adic distance is compatible with multiplication*, because:

$$r = p^n \frac{a_1}{b_1}, \quad r' = p^{n'} \frac{a_1'}{b_1'}, \quad rr' = p^{n+n'} \frac{a_1 a_1'}{b_1 b_1'}$$

leads to

$$|rr'|_p = h^{-(n+n')} = h^{-n} \cdot h^{-n'} = |r|_p \cdot |r'|_p$$

One can prove that in the field of rational numbers, the only distances that can be defined which are compatible with multiplication are the natural distance and the p-adic distance. This means that from the abstract and theoretical point of view these two definitions of distance, and these two alone, are well adapted to the deepest structure of the rational numbers. This is so true that the theory of numbers can be treated from the p-adic point of view (Hasse) and the demonstrations even become simplified because questions of multiples and divisors become translated into topological properties. Topology today is a well-developed science, handled with greater facility by modern mathematical scholars than the very difficult classical theory of integers.

Let us remark that the extension of the set of rational numbers to the set of p-adic numbers does not permit us to introduce an associated relation of order, while the notion of natural distance permits us to define the natural order in the set of rational numbers and in the complete set of real numbers.

Besides, the p-adic norm is not Archimedean; in effect: $|a + a + a \cdots + a|_p = |a|_p$, and we see that no matter how large an integer k is, the norm of ka does not exceed the norm of b.

Let us add that other fields than that of the rational numbers are encountered, for which we consider a distance compatible with multiplication; this is what we call a *valuation*. It is particularly true in the field of rational fractions with complex coefficients. In other words, the theory of valued fields arises in algebraic geometry, and we shall say a few words about it later.

We should mention a few other examples of composite structures.

If a set E has the structure of a group (designated, for example, multiplicatively) it is possible that a topology m may be defined on E of such kind that the function of two variables $f(x, y) = xy$ is continuous with respect to both x and y as they range over E. We then say that the *topology is compatible with the group structure* and that E has become a *topological group*. Such notions are encountered constantly in elementary geometry. For instance, let us take for E the set of plane similitudes; we can specify easily what we will mean by a "neighboring" similitude (neighboring centers, angles, ratios) and the product of two similitudes s_1' and s_2', neighbors respectively of s_1 and s_2, is a similitude neighboring the product $s_1 s_2$. We can similarly define a topological ring or a topological field.

Similarly, upon a vector space E defined on a topological field K, there can be defined a structure compatible with the structure of a vector space. For this topology, the function $f(v, w) = v + w$ is continuous for v and w which range over the space E, and the function $g(k, v) = kv$ is continuous for v which ranges over E and with respect to k which ranges over K. If this is so, the set E is said to be provided with the structure of a topological vector space. Such spaces are so frequently considered that they have been familiarly designated TVS.

We are naturally led to further refinements: for example a *Banach space* is a vector space upon the field of real or complex numbers; its topology is the one introduced by the following metric. Each element has a *norm*, a positive number satisfying:

(1) $$\| x \| = 0 \Leftrightarrow x = 0$$

(2) $$\| kx \| = |k| \, \| x \|$$

(3) $$\| x + y \| \leqq \| x \| + \| y \|$$

The *distance* of two points is the norm of their difference, and with this topology the space is finally complete (the Euclidean space of elementary geometry is evidently the most usual example of it).

Some Major Theories

Linear and multilinear algebra includes the study of linear equations and linear forms—the algebra of matrices and tensors. The point of view now held is that of mappings of one vector space upon another, which leads to matrices and to determinants for the linear forms. The bilinear forms are linear with respect to two sets of variables $x_1, x_2, \cdots, x_n$ and $y_1, y_2, \cdots, y_n$. The most important case is that in which x_i and y_i are conjugate complex numbers, the coefficients themselves being complex numbers; if the coefficients of $x_i y_j$ and of $x_j y_i$ are, besides, conjugates themselves, the bilinear form is real for all values of x_i and it is then called a *Hermitian form*. All these expressions are extremely useful, particularly in mechanics and in quantum theory. Besides, the linear character is so simple and convenient that we "linearize" the problems posed by physics by means of appropriate choices of new variables; we consider as components of an abstract linear space not only scalars, speeds, densities, but even sets of physical magnitudes in which the units that occur are not all the same. Thus "the algebra of matrices and

the algebra of tensors are extremely useful for a complete understanding of the most classical physics and they are indispensable
for a study of modern physics" (A. Lichnerowicz). Let us add that
linearization is essential for adapting computations to calculating
machines.

Algebraic geometry is the extension of the analytic geometry
of Descartes, which studies curves or surfaces by means of their
equations—polynomials equal to zero whose coefficients are real
numbers. We extend this study to the case in which the coefficients
are complex numbers and in which we study the "varieties" of a
space of n dimensions. Thus there are two practicable methods,
which, in a way, have become antagonistic to each other. One is
above all *geometric;* it utilizes intuition by constructing examples,
it willingly considers special cases, varieties having only singularities of simple types which it seeks to eliminate by suitable bira-
tional transformations. Although demonstrations in a certain re-
cent period may have been a little too much tinged with intuition
(see opinion of Severi in Chapter IV), they now can and should be
made rigorous. The other method that has arisen—*the abstract
method*—is described by André Weil as "essentially applicable to a
field with an arbitrary base." He goes on to say: "It is therefore
clear that in all cases where abstract proof is valid, we can hope
to attain more than by any classical demonstration of the same
result. . . . At present abstract methods by their very nature have
also the immense advantage of being able to be applied to varieties
with arbitrary singularities. . . . On the other hand it is often easier
to prove a theorem in a classical case and by a classical method.
. . . If a result which can be formulated in purely algebraic terms
is demonstrated in the classical case, it almost inevitably happens
that a corresponding result exists in the abstract theory. But what
the latter may be, that is precisely what it is not always easy to
guess." And this learned mathematician underlines his attitude—
after recognizing that "the algebraic varieties are subjects of considerable interest to analysts and topologists," he adds, "Nevertheless, from the point of view of algebraic geometry, it is undeniable
that the principal interest of the classical methods is to lead to

considering plausible results which it is then necessary to attack directly." Thus we see two tendencies which are antagonistic, certainly, but which are also complementary.

Infinitesimal geometry had been conceived as attaching geometric elements (tangents, tangent planes, curvature) to curves or surfaces defined by the equations that one derived. Now it is treated as a consequence of the topology of the space in which the "variety" is plunged. It is the "direct infinitesimal geometry," in Bouligand's words. We can, for example, study spaces of negative curvature without the hypothesis of differentiability. We define them axiomatically by attributing to them the properties studied by Hadamard in 1898 concerning the geodesics of surfaces with curvatures opposite to those of Euclidean space.

Analysis studies functions—no longer defined only on the field of real or complex numbers, but on sets furnished with algebraic structures—and associated topologies, a profound study of which had to be made in advance. For example, the examination of the demonstrations of Cauchy's theorems on continuous functions leads to the following precise and more general statements:

1. Every function defined and continuous on a *compact metric* space and with *real values* is bounded and attains its bounds.
2. Every function defined on a *compact metric* space E and with values in a *metric space* F, which is continuous on E, is uniformly continuous on E.
3. Every function defined and continuous on a *connected metric* space E and with *real values* takes for at least one point of E every value between the values taken at two points of E.

One of the theories of analysis that is developing with outstanding success is *harmonic analysis,* which extends the theory of Fourier (trigonometric and integral series) to extremely general areas, unifying theories which in appearance are far apart and "elucidating the mysterious character of certain results," as Braconnier remarks in *Mathematics Teaching.* He quotes André Weil:

"The locally compact Abelian groups form the natural domain of harmonic analysis."

A great novelty in analysis is the *theory of distributions* of Laurent Schwartz, which, remarkably, can take on a sufficiently simple form for it to be taught at the freshman level by the very man who created it. Let us quote from the preface of Schwartz's treatise, where he shows that the taking-off point of his discovery is the examination of the work of modern physicists: "To write that the Heaviside function (which is equal to 0 for $x < 0$ and to 1 for $x > 0$) has for its derivatives the function of Dirac $\sigma(x)$ (whose definition is mathematically contradictory), and to take the derivative of this supposed function—this is to exceed the limits permitted us. How can we explain the success of these methods? When such a contradictory situation presents itself, it is very rare that there does not result from it a new mathematical theory which justifies under a modified form the language of the physicists; there is even in this an important source of progress in mathematics and physics. . . . We have generalized the notion of function, first by that of measure, then by that of distribution. . . . The theory of the distributions is not an absolutely revolutionary novelty. This theory includes, in a fashion both simple and correct, some heterogeneous processes, often incorrect, used in very different domains: it is a synthesis and a simplification."

"Distributions constitute a correct mathematical definition of the distributions of charges met in physics." We know that if x is a variable and $f(x)$ is a suitable function, $\int_0^1 f(x)\,\mathrm{d}x$ is a number which depends on the function f. More generally, x will describe a space R^n of n dimensions, the functions $f(x)$ forming a topological vector space $\mathfrak{F}$ (with a suitable topology). This space will be formed of functions indefinitely derivable and with bounded support (they are zero outside of a bounded domain K of R^n). A distribution T is then a real or complex number attached to each function f in such a way that for all functions f, f_1, f_2 of the set $\mathfrak{F}$ and for every real or complex number k we have:

$$T(f_1 + f_2) = T(f_1) + T(f_2), \quad \text{and} \quad T(kf) = kT(f)$$

And also, that if f_i tends toward f_0 in the sense of the topology of $\mathfrak{F}$ when i tends towards infinity, $T(f_i)$ tends towards $T(f_0)$.

The conditions of differentiability imposed on the f functions seem narrow, but every continuous function with bounded support can be approximated by such functions. The theory of the differentiation of distributions is simpler than that of functions. Says Schwartz: "Distributions are to functions somewhat as complex numbers are to real numbers—every algebraic equation with real or complex coefficients has complex roots; every function locally summable or every distribution has successive derivatives of all orders which are distributions."

If we have been able to give a vague idea of what distributions are (they won for their creator the great gold medal at the 1950 International Congress of Mathematicians), we cannot do as much for other theories, such as that of "bundles" in cohomology and abstract algebraic geometry, which won for Jean-Pierre Serre the 1954 gold medal (if only there were Nobel prizes in mathematics!) or Gustave Choquet's theory of capacities, which binds the Newtonian capacity to probabilistic interpretations. All we shall say of them is that they are analogies of structures which have guided the mathematician in the construction of the extensions that unify the two extreme points of view.

We have just used the word "probabilistic." Although oriented by its innumerable applications now found in all of physics, probability is also, because of the idea of the *mean* which the theory itself introduces into mathematics, one of the areas of great activity in mathematics. For example, Kampe de Feriet observes that "the statistical mechanics of the turbulence of incompressible fluids demands the study of the transformations of the ring of the measurable functions in regard to a certain algebra where a topology is introduced." We quote this sentence only to emphasize the fundamental role of the two pillars, general algebra and general topology.

As for "stochastic processes," the study of which has been developing for about 20 years, we can understand their object from the following statement of Paul Levy:

"The idea of a stochastic process is, at least for a determinist, tied to that of the existence of hidden parameters which do not intervene in the description of the apparent present state of the system studied and which nevertheless influence its future evolution. Our ignorance of their values forces us to speak for the future only of a set of possible evolutions, and in certain cases we can define in that set a law of probability incessantly modified by the knowledge of new data."

Notions of stochastic continuity and of stochastic derivability have had to be created. On the other hand, it is not merely a question of numbers. We shall for example consider aleatory surfaces (skull forms, egg forms, etc.); we shall therefore need abstract theories on the sets of elements of some nature: thus we find again the same conditions imposed on modern science.

Conclusions

Here we end our rapid review of the present state of mathematics.* To pursue a simple enumeration, despite the underlying importance of the words, would be without interest. We nevertheless hope that we have justified the essential affirmations: mathematics studies abstract sets supplied with algebraic and topological structures. Mathematics is more and more comprehensive and polyvalent. Its progress is made principally by extension of the starting set of each theory with the aim of generalizing the properties and of unifying the theories that have certain common structures—thus, "synthesis and simplification," as Schwartz says.

Now that we have varied examples at our disposal, we can return briefly to this idea of extension of a theory. The oldest extensions, from natural integers to rational numbers to signed numbers to irrational numbers to imaginary numbers, were made in order to make possible certain operations (division, subtraction, extraction of roots, solution of equations) which in the initial set were impossible.

* For further reading, see the series of articles by G. Bouligand, "At the Heart of Mathematics," in the *Revue generale des Sciences*, 1956–57.

More modern extensions transform the very definition of the operations by enlarging it. A typical example is the creation of the Lebesgue integral. Let us quote here from his *Preface to Lessons on Integration* of 1903: "We may ask if there is any point in limiting oneself to the study of well-behaved functions which require only simple definitions. But it would then be necessary to renounce the resolution of many problems with simple terms set long ago. It is for the resolution of these problems and not for the love of complications that I have introduced a definition of the integral more general than Riemann's and including his as a special case. . . . I dare say that this definition is in a certain sense simpler than Riemann's and as easy to grasp as his; only mental habits acquired earlier can make it seem more complicated. It is simpler because it shows the most important properties of the integral, while Riemann's definition shows only a process of calculation. . . . Even if we are interested only in the results relative to the simple functions, it is useful to know the notion of summable functions because it suggests rapid procedures of demonstration."

Lebesgue's conclusion was that every problem comes back to joining two magnitudes attached to arbitrary domains and a function attached to a point of these areas: "Integration is always an operation analogous to that which is necessary in order to evaluate the *quantity of heat necessary* to raise the temperature of a body by 1° as a function of the *masses* of its parts and of the *specific heat at each point.*" Schwartz's extension consists in creating this function at a point where it does not exist; if the charges (or masses) exist in only one or several points, we cannot define the density $f(x)$ as a function to be integrated; a distribution will play the role of this non-existent function.

A third type of extension preserves the definition of the operations but modifies the structure which these operations impose on the set after the adjunction of new elements. Naturally it is always a question of simplifying the structure to permit demonstrations. Thus the introduction of ideals in a ring $\mathcal{C}$ to make of them a set of $\mathcal{B}$ will permit us to assure the uniqueness factorization in irreducible elements. We might think that this extension would not interest those who study the ring $\mathcal{C}$. But to leave $\mathcal{C}$ temporarily in order to operate in $\mathcal{B}$, which is easier, permits the enunciation of general consequences for $\mathcal{B}$ which are valid in $\mathcal{C}$. We again find familiar ideas such as introducing imaginary points in geometry to demonstrate properties of the real domain, or reasoning in three-dimensional space to obtain a result of plane geometry, or even utilizing a path in the complex plane in order to calculate a definite integral. As we have said, it is using a stronger theory as a model of the theory to be studied.

We conclude with the statement that modern mathematics is in continuity with earlier mathematics whose work it extends. As usual, this is not done without some collisions, but now more than ever it changes the aspect of the science more rapidly, it changes the extent of its results, the choice of entities studied, and the tools of its work. On the other hand, mathematics is more than ever in contact with other sciences, and with physics in particular, since these two sciences find subjects of mutual inspiration and help each other in the march toward future progress.

VI

*Ah, then you advise us to read Bour-
baki to our pupils?*

—TEACHER (ANON.)

THE PEDAGOGIC
POINT OF VIEW

With a last glance of admiration, of regret, and even of envy, let
us leave the learned theories we have glimpsed to the mathematicians and to the physicists and engineers in all specialties who use
them. We know that all these theories are beautiful, and, what is
more, useful, because they contribute to clarifying and supporting
one another and because they are already, or will be some day,
indispensable for their sister sciences. As for what may prove useful
to the modest technicians that most of our science students will
become, it is impossible to mark out the field precisely. For the
greatest number, linear and multilinear algebra, matrices and tensors will probably be in current use—but a young aeronautics en-
gineer whose job it is to interpret laboratory experiments tells me
that he uses only polynomials of the fifth degree. Harmonic analysis
will be an indispensable tool for some physiologists or workers in
electricity. Cybernetics uses the theory of relations, and statistics
the calculus of sets.

The list of indispensable subjects grows ever longer, but it is
not a question of teaching everybody everything in the same way.
The essential thing is that the student, before specialization, be led
to the level of thought and knowledge that will allow him to be
initiated into the techniques that he may later choose. The teaching
of advanced mathematics, pure or oriented toward applications, is
the business of the colleges and the universities; we shall say
nothing of it. For the secondary-school teacher and—why not?—

for the primary-school teacher, a certain understanding of modern mathematics is necessary if he is to transmit to his students an idea which may be rudimentary but must not be a caricature. This understanding of the science will also clarify the reactions and resistances of the pupils.

Elementary Mathematics

For those who have no mathematical knowledge beyond their several-years-old memory of their school lessons, the impression of entering a foreign land may be fairly violent. One begins to wonder where among our old mathematical learnings are hidden the notions now being brought forward, and, conversely, to what limbo modern mathematics has relegated what we used to call elementary mathematics (and what is indeed still at least a *part* of elementary mathematics).

Answering the first question is easy enough. One teacher, after his first contact with the algebra of sets, said: "I had always thought the simplest operation was addition." But a child in kindergarten knows that the first thing one must do is to differentiate collections and classify objects. The small child is initiated into the relation of order by arranging unequal cubes; he will learn to distinguish a yellow bouquet from one that includes some yellow flowers, and he will understand the inclusion of sets. But these mental operations seem too simple to be called "mathematics," and the teacher who teaches them to the child probably does not know that she is starting his mathematical development, perhaps with decisive influence. Similarly all topological observations—coloring in designs, paper-cutting—are a preparation for geometry long before the notions of squares or isosceles triangles.

That all this should afterward remain implicit in the program need surprise no one. It is always the deepest root that remains hidden and unknown; it is the hardest to analyze, to bring to the conscious level. All this initiation is so well forgotten by adults that when we are invited to examine a domain which extends immediately the apprenticeship of the kindergarten, we are as ill at ease as when we move with our big feet among the tiny chairs and low tables where the children do their elementary algebra and topology! The initiation forgotten, our civilized world uses its results to such an extent that we cannot imagine how one could think without these pieces of knowledge. Yet the elementary concepts are so thoroughly taken for granted that we don't think of pointing them out to the schoolboy when we "really" start reasoned mathematics, so sure are we that he thinks as we do; we have not even felt it necessary to have a vocabulary or symbols to express them, so that the words now applied to them—terms such as "union," "intersection," "complementary," "connected"—seem recondite and a little stilted. The fact that we ourselves have neglected to give conscious thought to these elementary and fundamental matters—doesn't that make us as teachers reluctant to impose it on the child, lest we interrupt his natural mental development, in somewhat the same way as when we require him to do plane geometry at the age when he is interested in construction and mechanics? Moreover, if attention to the foundations does not lead him to a science with true mathematical value but only toward artificial and poor school-mathematics, good only for examinations, what excuse shall we have?

Excuses we can certainly find, and we can even say there is nothing to excuse. Since the foundations of mathematics were unconscious, and since mathematicians nevertheless have lost no esteem on that account, may not these foundations properly remain unconscious for the pupils, to whom we do not pretend to teach "mathematics" but only a little computation and a few theorems in geometry? This is saying that what has lasted so long can last longer! But to shut one's eyes to what is "modern" is at the same time a refusal to see the past; one then believes that teaching can be only what it is, and one forgets what it was, and even what it is in other countries. It was not so long ago that the theorem of Chasles was introduced into elementary teaching and began to be used in geometry from the first years on; not so long ago that mathematicians began to associate with each theorem its converse or converses. (The 1810 *Treatise on Converses* by Garnier emphasizes the omission of this association. Legendre, for example, gave the theorem on the diagonals of a rectangle without its converse alongside; each theorem was introduced only to describe a particular figure, but not to characterize it. Moreover, this attitude still exists here and there in the manuals; for example, authors often omit demonstrating that the classic inequalities among the faces of a trihedral form a system sufficient to assure the existence of the trihedral.)

Is it certain that the fortunate introduction of graphs, of vectors, of oriented angles, marks the end of realizable progress? We shall say nothing about the theories which it would perhaps be necessary to introduce, or about what might be cut out; we shall only seek to show by some examples how the modern point of view can help us in elementary instruction, whatever the material taught.

But we proposed another question: What has become of the old elementary mathematics in the present architecture? We are especially struck by the rearrangement of old topics, which are no longer grouped by subject but by structures. Classification is made by different criteria, so that even if nothing has changed in the statements we consider, and even if they keep a particular character in relation to the object concerned, relationships among them are changed. In a book intended for farmers, the chapter on rabbits may be next to that on chickens; the same chapter may speak of the work-horse and the tractor. But is this acceptable in a zoology text? In books that claim to construct geometry we find a chapter entitled "concurrent lines in a triangle"—as one might say "animals of the barnyard"—where medians are mixed with altitudes and bisectors, like rabbits with chickens. Such books confuse lessons about things with zoology; they confuse a problem ("what can one see in a triangle?") with a logical exposition—"hypothetico-deductive," in Bouligand's phrase. Perhaps this is all right for children. But the teacher ought to know what he is doing, to direct his teaching on the basis of his knowledge, and to coordinate his conclusions.

Thus we find our old knowledge again, under new titles. Even if we decide to keep the traditional order for the earliest teaching, with our modern awareness we shall be able to impart a better understanding which will later enable the student to conceive the possibility of a unifying axiomatization. Thus the notion of the application of one set onto another will unify our concept of operations, of point transformations, of functions with their double aspect—algebraic and topological. We shall think of the relation of order in studying divisibility. We shall compare the uniqueness of the decomposition of an integer or of a polynomial into the product of irreducible factors and the decomposition of a displacement into products of symmetries. We shall demonstrate the neutral elements of all kinds of operations. We shall compare the relation of Chasles for vectors and for angles. Perhaps we shall know whether or not the fractional exponents are fractions!

Naturally when one has just moved into a new apartment, one is at first upset at not finding the old furnishings in their customary places. It becomes necessary to sacrifice out-of-date and not very useful articles and procure more purposeful new ones. Every change of residence is to some extent a catastrophe for the person involved; but people quickly become accustomed to the new, especially young people who have not known the old house and find modern comfort and new styles very natural. If one is convinced that improvements are possible, he must prepare for them; it is therefore to a sincere examination of conscience, after a thorough study, that we are invited.

Logic and Formalism

In Chapter IV we pointed out the possibility of presenting logical deductions and statements under the form of relations among sets. This is something extremely important for our teaching, since the child sees objects globally without clearly distinguishing their properties. He more clearly understands a set of rectangles, of which he can draw some examples, than he can compare the statements "having right angles," "having equal diagonals." If we say, "we are interested in quadrilaterals; we are considering all those with equal diagonals; among them are all rectangles," they will ask without prompting: "Are there any which are not rectangles?" And they will draw some, probably even without having asked themselves the question. If one says only, in the usual way, "If a quadrilateral is a rectangle, its diagonals are equal," how many will clearly perceive the converse and the need to demonstrate it?

The translation of the usual statements, especially if they are at all complex and require qualification, is a very instructive exercise; we shall give some examples in the Appendix. But here we emphasize a different point of view: Theorems must be *used* in the exercises. It follows that an active, dynamic form of statement is indispensable for beginners. In place of the two static statements above, we shall propose: "Each time I know that a quadrilateral is a rectangle, I shall deduce from that that its diagonals are equal." There is here an indication of a "direction of an open road," but it is a one-way road, and one can fix it in his memory—visual memory, logical memory, memory of what one can do—by adopting the symbol $\Rightarrow$ and writing:

$$\boxed{\text{The quadrilateral is a rectangle}} \Rightarrow \boxed{\text{Diagonals are equal}}$$

And when we speak of parallelograms we can write:

$$\boxed{\text{rectangles}} \Leftrightarrow \boxed{\text{equal diagonals}}$$

Here we are brought to the question of formalism. The first symbol we meet is even more than a logical sign, a schematic sign. It is all the more accepted by the pupil because it is, after all, connected with roadsigns! Our children, especially in cities, see around them innumerable symbols which they understand better, and much faster, than sentences! The red light stops traffic better than any placard, and if the "Pedestrians Wait" signs one sees were not colored in this symbolic red, they would have little effect. The use of color to suggest relationships is very valuable: it is one of the best symbols pedagogy can employ. It is one of the elements of success of Cuisenaire's and Gattegno's "numbers in color" of which we shall speak briefly later. Besides, many teachers use color to

Now these two uniform structures are not comparable, that is to say, given an ϵ, there is no ϵ' such that:

$$\forall r, \forall r', \quad r \, W_{\epsilon'} r' \quad \text{assures} \quad r \, N_\epsilon r'$$

And conversely, given an ϵ', there is no ϵ such that

$$\forall r, \forall r', \quad r \, N_\epsilon r' \quad \text{assures} \quad r \, W_{\epsilon'} r'$$

In fact, by definition,

$$r \, W_{\epsilon'} r' \Leftrightarrow [\,|r - r'| < r \cdot \epsilon' \quad \text{and} \quad |r - r'| < r' \cdot \epsilon'\,]$$

which cannot be guaranteed by $|r - r'| < \epsilon$ for all numbers r and r' because these can be as close to zero as we wish.

Similarly, the second condition cannot guarantee the first one for all numbers r and r', because these numbers can be as large as we wish.

But the topology associated to the metric introduced in (1) permits us to define for any given number a and for all positive $\alpha < a$, "a neighborhood of a of order α": it is the set of numbers r which satisfies:

$$d(r, a) < \alpha,$$

that is to say,

$$|r - a| < \alpha, \quad \text{or} \quad a - \alpha < r < a + \alpha$$

Let us designate this condition by $r \, T_\alpha a$.

If r and r' are in the neighborhood of a of a small enough order α, they are also as close to each other as we wish, in the sense of (1) and (2).

This means, more exactly, that given a, if ϵ and ϵ' are chosen positive and less than a,

$$\forall \epsilon, \, \exists \alpha : [r \, T_\alpha a \quad \text{and} \quad r' \, T_\alpha a] \Rightarrow r \, N_\epsilon r'$$

and
$$\forall \epsilon', \, \exists \beta : [r \, T_\beta a \quad \text{and} \quad r' \, T_\beta a] \Rightarrow r \, W_{\epsilon'} r'$$

Actually, we need merely take:

$$\alpha < \frac{a}{2}, \quad \beta < \frac{\epsilon(a - \epsilon)}{2}$$

make figures more expressive, as the choice of notation makes algebraic formulas expressive.

But let us return to the sign of inference used in the diagrams. Just as formalism alone permitted abstract research on the non-contradiction of mathematics, a diagram permits the pupil to check with a glance whether a reasoning is correctly constructed, then to check each step somewhat as we check an algebraic calculation line by line. At the same time, the teacher can become aware of the complexity of the solution of an exercise. Let us take the following example—a study of a triangle one of whose angle bisectors is a median.

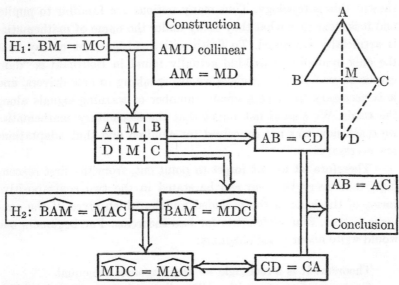

We observe that obviously the idea of making a construction requires a certain experience with making use of medians. And the beginner must find in the statement the necessary guide, must know how to read, must be confident. This is perhaps the place to underline that not everything comes "naturally," that one must have a flair, some imagination, together with knowledge ready to be put to use; a certain amount of genius is required. Hermann Weyl has remarked: "The theory of invariables burst upon the world, somewhat like Minerva, about the middle of the nineteenth century; an adult virgin covered with the sparkling armor of algebra, she leaped from the head of Jupiter—Cayley."

The study of conjunctions to be used in directing the diagrammed demonstration above is an excellent exercise; it is absolutely necessary to introduce "but" or "on the other hand."

Let us note that other diagrams familiar to all can serve as introductions to topology. For example, in buses, passengers can look out of the windows and see the more or less twisting form of the actual trip: this is geography. But in the subway the trip appears as a straight line and only the intersections and forks are shown: this is topology. Thus many notions are familiar to pupils, and it is clear that what they study under the name of mathematics is artificially restricted. To finish with roadsigns, let us say that the only symbol of this kind actually found in Bourbaki is "dangerous curve." But as teachers we are speaking to new drivers, and it is necessary to place a greater number of warning signals along the roads. We should not forget that the elementary mathematics we teach now was not conceived for children and that adaptations are necessary.

Therefore let us not forget to point out, from the first reasonings, that every theorem can be stated in the two contrapositive forms of the logic of the excluded middle, which gives, if the converse is true, four statements for two theorems. For beginners one would write about parallelograms:

Theorem: It is a rectangle $\Rightarrow$ the diagonals are equal.
Contrapositive proposition: The diagonals are unequal $\Rightarrow$ it is not a rectangle.

Converse: The diagonals are equal $\Rightarrow$ it is a rectangle.
Contrapositive proposition: It is not a rectangle $\Rightarrow$ the diagonals are not equal.

This is a revelation for children of 13 or 14, and they are greatly interested in these points of logic, which, with rare exceptions, they have never noticed. Reasoning by absurdity, which they can then understand by enumeration of cases, pleases them with its comic nuances, which the teacher's tone of voice emphasizes.

In the process of writing up any material, the use of several symbols does not mean the use of an entirely formalized language. Two main aims, it seems, ought to guide us: on the one hand, to introduce a symbol that will emphasize the essential idea of the moment; on the other hand, to standardize the forms of the important statements and reasonings to remember. Our common language, as a matter of fact, is so supple, so capable of shades of meaning, that it can dress them in a thousand suits colored by intuition and even by varied emotions.

It is up to us as experienced teachers to discover the essential idea and bring it into the open. From the mathematical point of view, all the elements of a statement are equally indispensable, but we know that the beginner often leaves part of it in the shade; it is these elements that must be emphasized. We have already seen the "one way only" of the implication opposed to the "both ways permitted" of the equivalence. For expressions of elementary algebra, the notion to bring out is the distributive law, in which addition and multiplication play different roles. Why not underline this distinction by using during the necessary time (a month or two, for example) symbols like $(a + b) \times c$ and $\boxed{a \times b} + c$, the closed box signifying "distributivity forbidden"? Later this will be indicated by "gluing" the letters a and b to make $ab + c$, but this is impossible with written numbers in ordinary numeration—it *is* possible with fractions. Will someone say this is childish and not very mathematical? But Bourbaki himself recognizes that "the formulas of ordinary algebraic calculation would be a formalized text if there had been complete codification of the rules governing the use of parentheses and if they were strictly observed, whereas actually certain of these rules are learned chiefly by use, and use permits certain departures."

For the approach to geometric loci, the essential idea is that of *belonging to*, and the key to transmitting it is the use of a special symbol. We said that the sign $\in$ has been adopted (from the initial epsilon of the verb $\epsilon\sigma\tau\iota$). The question posed in trying to find a geometric locus can be put into standardized form as follows:

Domain: The points of a plane, or of a half plane, or of space. . . . We distinguish some points that fit (for example, equidistant from two given points A and B). We seek $\mathfrak{C}$, a figure (line or segment or union of two rays or an arc of a circle, etc.) such that we can state:

$$\boxed{\text{M} \in \mathfrak{C}} \Leftrightarrow \boxed{\text{M fits}}$$

All teachers (and they are now numerous) who use the symbol of "belonging to" ($\in$) agree that it is perfectly satisfactory to the child.

In other chapters the universal quantifier $\forall$ marks the essential idea, particularly for the point transformations (translation expressed by $\forall \text{M}, \overrightarrow{\text{MM}'} = \overrightarrow{\text{V}}$) or for algebraic identities. The use of the symbol is even more satisfactory to the student in that it replaces a long assemblage of signs, dangerous from an orthographic point of view. To write "$\forall \text{M}, \forall x_0$ and x_1" is more practical than "whatever M is; whatever x_0 and x_1 are" or "whatever be the values of x_0 and x_1."

But clearly one can be led to multiply the symbols, to write, for example, $\forall x, x \in \text{E}$ (for any x, x belonging to E). A teacher will or will not write it according to the situation; it is pedagogically a question of tact. Thus, in the body of the work, Bourbaki uses the sign of belonging but not the quantifier. We find, "for every $x, x \in \text{E}$" or "$e \in \text{H}_i$ for any i"! But there is a difference between a written exposition and a resumé written on the board or notes taken at top speed; there is too much tendency to write at the board only equalities or inequalities, and the pupils do hardly more than copy them. Once attention has been drawn to the importance of quantifiers, the resumé will no longer omit the essential idea, and, like speakers at faculty meetings, everyone will take the trouble, if he does not care to use symbols, to write everything out: "whatever may be" or "there exists at least one." As for the pupils, they without any doubt prefer the symbols if they are accustomed to them.

We know how widespread is the habit of abbreviations of all kinds; they meet a need, but they are dangerous when they are anarchic and ambiguous. It is up to us to show that the symbols of relations or of operations are different from abbreviations, and that they are strictly codified. It is to avoid wrong meanings that it seems wise to reserve the double arrow $\Rightarrow$ for the logical implication, the sign $\rightarrow$ for the indication of "tends toward a limit" and the sign $\curvearrowright$ to the idea "corresponds to."

The Natural Language and the Language of Mathematics

We do not forget that the teacher of mathematics, like his colleagues in other subjects, is also a teacher of ordinary language; his task from that point of view is to teach a correct and logical language which will translate a clear thought exactly. If, from the artistic point of view, form precedes thought and orients it by its rhythm or accent, logical language, on the other hand, supposes an exact thought coming first, and our difficulties are multiplied if we demand of a child a suitable expression at the very moment of the effort to understand: it widens the separation between our thought and his if we try to transmit the thought by means of a vocabulary and a syntax which are strangers to him. What a fine understanding results if we can remain silent, express ourselves by gesture, and not interpose a curtain of words between the mathematical relation and the thought! But not everything can be expressed in gestures, especially since we have to assist memory. Let us not forget that time is an essential element of reasoning, which is a succession of thoughts. When thought has been formalized, or conceived of as formalizable, the work of correct phrasing can begin—work done collectively, work which makes exact both the nuance of thought and the sense of translating the words, work which gives a keen satisfaction, for, even if it is not precisely mathematical, it is the crowning of the mathematical project.

Formalism is thus conceived as an intermediary between mathematical thought (a perception of causal dependence, of relations of equivalence or of belonging, of possibilities of deduction) and its expression—impersonal, fixed, "frozen" for shipment, so to speak, and requiring to be revived **upon** receipt. The language of mathematics is not entirely the natural language; it is more concise, loaded with conjunctions, every word having an exact significance. We have already said that alongside the formalized parts and the language of mathematics there is room, too, for the ordinary language that calls upon intuition, invites to comparisons, announces future prolongations, and so on. The beginner must be warned of this distinction when he is invited to do the phrasing himself.

Exposition of the Whole

If we move from the form to the substance, if we consider the fundamental statements of the first year of geometry, for example, it is not necessary to begin by denying that children know them or believe they know them. They do not doubt that a triangle with two equal sides also has two equal angles, nor that a rectangle has equal diagonals. The task is not to teach them these things as novelties; it is more important to make them experience the emotion produced by the acquisition of knowledge through reasoning—for example, learning of the existence of four circles tangent to three lines—*any* lines—despite the doubts raised by imperfect diagrams. And yet, how can we reason if we start from nothing? We come to the thorny question of deciding whether one can make an axiomatic explanation in teaching at the secondary level.

Let us ignore the sneer (akin to "Ah, then 2 plus 2 will now make 5?") of the skeptic who now asks: "Ah, then you advise us to read Bourbaki to our pupils?" The best answer is to quote the "method of use" of the Bourbaki treatise. It takes mathematics at the beginning and gives complete demonstrations. A reading of the treatise therefore does not in principle suppose any particular mathematical knowledge but only a certain habit of mathematical reasoning and a certain power of abstraction. Nevertheless this work is indeed intended particularly for readers who possess at least a good knowledge of general mathematics and, if possible, of the essential parts of a course in integral and differential calculus.

Thus, in order to understand an axiomatic, it is necessary to have the habit of mathematical reasoning, the power of abstraction and a "good" knowledge of certain questions in the area to be axiomatized.

Still, teachers in our secondary schools very often presume to make a rigid deductive exposition after a few sentences which are axioms, whether or not they are so identified; they pretend to pure reasoning, to proceeding from definitions to demonstrations of theorems and corollaries with no appeal to intuition. But when one examines the school texts, one sees everywhere holes in the reasoning (most especially where topology is concerned); the construction of the whole, besides, is scarcely legitimate—now explaining a theory, now organized around the description of an important figure. But since that is necessary, it would be better that the teacher realize it clearly.

When one has himself struggled with diverse axiomatic constructions, one realizes that he cannot begin to move about comfortably until an adequate intuition has developed, an intuition which, to quote Bourbaki, "is not necessarily of a spatial or sense nature, as is sometimes thought, but which is rather a certain knowledge of the behavior of mathematical beings, helped often by images of a very varied nature but based above all on daily frequentation of them."

A premature axiomatic is impossible (in geometry particularly) because, on the one hand, the child is incapable of understanding and remembering long chains of reasoning, and, on the other hand, he is very demanding of details and rigid in his understanding, which would make it necessary to tell all. The rigidity of pupils is well known: "A square is not a rectangle." "Zero is not a number since it is *nothing*." Their demand for explanations is illustrated by the following typical challenges from fifth-graders: "If the points M of the interior of a circle with center O of radius R are defined by $OM < R$, O is not on the inside because there is no longer an OM." "You say 3 plus 6 equals 9—but 9 is also 4 plus 5." "Nobody said that halves of equal angles are also equal." "To say that after a prime number there is always another, is that *exactly* the same thing as saying there is an infinity of them?" "You said that two opposite numbers have the *same* absolute value but different signs; then −2/3 and +4/6 are not opposite?" This last challenge was put to me by a little thirteen-year-old girl in a tone of such irony that I realized more than ever how necessary it is to be strict and exact with ourselves, in order to be worthy of teaching children.

We are then tempted to conclude that if many children do not understand mathematics, it is because our teaching is not axiomatic enough; but that on the other hand, our pupils are incapable of following an axiomatic. Well, then, what is to be done? Our program might be to show the basic notions of mathematics in the course of activities of all sorts, particularly in practical works, calculations, and geometric constructions with various instruments. In bringing the student to recognize and compare mathematical structures as a means of making correct applications and elementary logical deductions, one would be laying the groundwork for an axiomatized science which could be at least introduced in part in elementary school and followed with progressive understanding in a secondary school.

Elementary and Secondary Courses

To begin with, we must take as our starting point the general knowledge the child has acquired in his premathematical experimentation and must analyze the properties of his items of knowledge in the manner of the natural sciences. This analysis should precede any definition, so that, as Lebesgue says, "what one demonstrates appears clearly to the eyes of all as a logical legitimization of facts already known, accepted and used." Certain of these facts will become definitions or axioms or theorems of a theory.

For example, let us recognize that the isosceles triangle is a familiar object to the child in the fourth or fifth grade but his knowledge is global; that is, the properties of the triangle are perceived chaotically. Our aim will be to have him see a meaningful scheme, which will later be enriched.

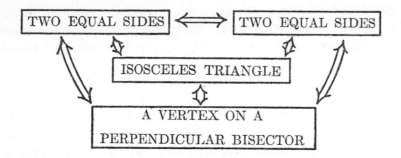

Some teachers think it scandalous not to begin with a definition learned by heart—in this case, naturally, the definition of the isosceles triangle as a triangle with two equal sides. I confess that I do not understand this attitude, and if I submit to the conventional practice, it is only simple conformity, like that of the good pupil, who knows that he must recite this sacred sentence to get a good mark.

From my point of view, if one *must* start with a preliminary definition, it would be better to choose the characteristic property of the perpendicular bisector. Will objections be raised with respect to the origin of the word "isosceles"? Well, then, let us define a triangle as a figure having three angles. It suffices to enumerate the triangle, the quadrilateral, the pentagon—etymology has its place in our historic remarks but not in the logical construction of mathematics.

The study of parallelograms is the occasion for analogous diagrams and for a similar observation: for me, in all sincerity, as for the child, a rectangle is not "defined" when we say it is "a parallelogram which has a right angle." It is essential, it seems to me, to complete the study at this point by demonstrating inclusion, union, and intersection of classes of quadrilaterals.

Definition is a mathematical and logical act, too essential to be confused with simple *naming*. True definitions are not lacking in the first lessons of elementary mathematics, and they must be made with care. Sometimes the word to be defined is the label attributed to an entity constructed in the interior of the theory and important enough so that diverse characterizations have been sought for it; the naming comes when the object is well distinguished from other objects of the theory. Or, and this is more serious, one creates a new notion which leads to an extension of the theory.

As an example of the first type, consider the circles tangent to the three sides of a triangle; the naming must necessarily follow not only the demonstration of existence but also the description of a construction. A definition by demonstration of a thing's existence (such as that of the lowest common multiple of two numbers) is not satisfying to the child—he requires a definition by construction.

Of the second type is the definition of the distance from a point to a line. Here is an opportunity to have the child reflect on what a distance is. What one can tell him about the distance between two points cannot interest him, for that notion is too familiar. But he doesn't really have the notion of the distance from a point to a set, or from one set to another, although he feels in a confused fashion what must be done to make such a notion precise. We must legitimatize the use of the word "distance" and lay a groundwork, as even the author of a learned book does before he brings himself to say: "We are now able to define a distance."

Another essential definition, for lack of which children understand nothing about the use of fractions, is that of *rational number;* it crowns that of *equivalent fractions,* which one ends by calling "equal" but which are never "the same." So long as all calculations on fractions are justified by recourse to pies or ribbons, algebra is impossible, and an intelligent non-conformist child is led to ask (and *did* ask in the third grade!) if one can *always* replace 4/6 by 2/3 in the solution of a system of equations given in the abstract.

At the beginning of the secondary course there is an opportunity to review and put to use the notions introduced up to that point. Can one at this stage give an axiomatic exposition? In arithmetic and algebra, where axiomatization would be relatively easy, there is something better to do, for the child has not yet had enough training for computation (especially with so little time devoted to mathematics in schools at the present time). The teacher can confine himself at first to the more modest aim of helping students to put structures to use—structures abstracted simultaneously from objects counted or measured and from special values of numbers introduced. Thus he frees himself from the strict order imposed by the choice of an axiomatic introduction. In geometry an axiomatic exposition is clearly impossible; still we can organize material on the basis of an implied axiomatic, the course of which will follow broad lines and will permit the progressive revelation to the pupil of the possibility of various axiomatic constructions. It seems acceptable, for example, to start with a metric, so familiar to pupils of that age, and then go on to isometrics. We know the failure of attempts to start with the point transformations by translation or rotation. These complex notions, especially the notion of general point (or variable point), that is, of the precise meaning of the universal quantifier $\forall$, are not suitable for beginners. On the contrary, symmetry with respect to a line in a plane (reflection) or with respect to a plane in space seems acceptable to coordinate the known facts and to structure the exposition. The bifurcation toward the geometry of Lobachevsky is apparent; the affine geometry disengages itself bit by bit, after the introduction of parallels, with the introduction of vectors, and even projective geometry comes into view: weaker and weaker theories thus appear by progressive diminution of the set of objects distinguished and of the set of properties defined for the objects and, consequently, by enlargement of the equivalence classes which become the true objects that the theory studies.

Our fine terminal class in elementary mathematics is really the one where an axiomatic construction can be undertaken even if it must be limited to the most essential scaffoldings and if the brick-by-brick construction of the edifice must be renounced. The experience already acquired by the pupil provides the relations of the theories to be axiomatized; the habit of mathematical reasoning is inculcated and the faculty of abstraction is adequate: these are the conditions already enumerated as necessary. As one starts again at the very base, arithmetic and algebra, one clearly starts with numbers. A sketch of topology permits the study of functions; on the other hand, the introduction of topological vector spaces introduces affine geometry. One approaches geometry through its intermediate form which, by weakening, leads to projective geometry and by reinforcement to metric Euclidean geometry. The pedagogic question that remains delicate is the insertion of the "metric grafting stem" because pupils who find familiar territory burn up the road and grow impatient. It is probably better to accept a speedy passage, limiting oneself to indications. A little later some steps in anallagmatic geometry (where the elementary transformation is the inversion) will permit a return to the thought of a system of axioms suitable to the geometry one wishes to construct. At this stage, it is conceivable that various systems of axioms will lead straight to the target (such as Hilbert's for metric geometry or Choquet's by isometries).

Are the reflections in this book of any use for very young children, just being initiated into the beginnings of computation? We said that if abstract structures must first be observed in the real and finally rediscovered for application, mathematics nevertheless considers them for their own sake. Let us accept the necessity of these three attitudes in the first teaching of mathematics. But are children primarily observers? Do they make abstractions? Are they technicians? Here are two authentic anecdotes which I present without comment.

A very young child was asked by his grandfather, "I have seven apples, I take away three, how many do I now have?" The child made no answer, until, no longer able to restrain his exasperation, he finally demanded, "But what did you do with those three apples?" Said the grandfather, "I ate them." Then, relieved, the child went on to answer quickly, "There are four left." The child could not compute while he was thinking about the apples!

I told this to a friend, and she confided, in a tone almost of emotion, a secret memory of her childhood: "I was about five. I was counting aloud as my mother had taught me, 'three apps and four apps, that makes seven apps.' Someone present praised my

mother for this concrete method of teaching, which must be so
effective for a child—to invoke apples in this way. I almost fainted;
this ritual word 'apps' that I used in counting, did it actually
stand for real fruit? Something like a feeling of shame came over
me—after that I never mentioned apples again in counting."

A remarkable example of what understanding of structures
can bring to teaching is furnished by a new method of instruction
which introduces arithmetic by means of "little color rods." It was
invented by the Belgian teacher G. Cuisenaire and perfected by
C. Gattegno. With almost no words or written symbols, by means
of unconscious manipulations and observations, this method brings
into the set of integers (at first only the small numbers but soon
passing beyond 100) and also into the set of simple fractions, the
structure of order—the structure of a ring for the integers and the
structure of the field for the rational numbers. It is certainly a matter of the structures themselves, for the operations are done simultaneously on numbers, on lengths and on colors, therefore actually
on an abstract set. The equipment includes only small rods
divided into square sections one centimeter on a side, and a set of
cubes. The 1-centimeter cube is white, the 2-centimeter cube red,
the 3-centimeter cube green, and so on up to 10 centimeters. The 2,
4, and 8 cubes form one color family, 3, 6, and 9 another, and 5 and
10 a third; 7 is black. Addition consists in putting cubes end to
end, and the relation of equivalence is superposition. Useless to
give definitions! The relation of order is obvious, and a few manipulations assure a perfect knowledge of the commutativity and the
associativity of addition, as well as the properties of the inverse
operation. It is observed that the child, particularly if very young,
quickly separates himself from number and length. He operates
with amazing rapidity on the colors—showing him a tiny corner of
the rod suffices to make him understand what element of the set
is called for. A simple convention symbolizes multiplication, and
the ring structure appears with all its properties. The most curious
thing to notice is the ease with which the rational number is introduced: on seeing the rods, the small child immediately answers the
question: "If this is one, what is this other?" the answer being, for

example, 4/5. Similarly, to compute 7/5 + 2/3 the intermediary of 21/15 + 10/15 is needed; to compute 7/5 × 2/3 the intermediary 14/10 × 10/15 is needed; the multiplication is done by removing the two rods which are side by side, having become simple relays in the comparison.

To appreciate the extraordinary success of the method, one has to see it in operation. Gattegno has perfected it by using it with various classes—retarded children, gifted children, deaf-mutes, etc. Even a poor abnormal child in a little Italian village was able to respond to the subject of inverse fractions after about ten minutes of manipulation of the rods. (Under the auspices of UNESCO Gattegno has introduced the method in Ethiopia.) Naturally one also trains the child to recognize the operations in actual life and one teaches him to write the customary symbols. After a while the child gives up the rods and calculates with numbers. This is not a failure; on the contrary, it is the desired goal (from the point of view of calculation at least), just as extra stabilizing wheels on a child's bicycle may be removed when the child becomes able to balance himself on two wheels. The rods serve only to set forth with one gesture and a few words the proposed exercises and to check them. But because of their ability to show diverse structures, the rods have many applications: in particular, they can also be used to make precise the notions of volume and area (by sliding the rods one over the other, for example), and always with a minimum of words.

Conclusions for the Teacher

Every conscientious teacher makes an effort to present what can be understood by his pupils, what can be useful to them, but also what he believes to be true. He transmits a technique, and also a thought. If a given procedure in calculation is part of an apprenticeship, knowledge of a science is part of general culture. What is the value of a particular theorem? Is it a curious statement, an elegant property, or perhaps an essential part of the architecture of a theory? Is it the historic remains of an ancient theory? And is its statement revelatory of an outdated thought or is it perhaps the anticipation of a theory which is not part of the class program but the study of which prepares the approach to later research? We see the mutual assistance of the history of scientific thought and the study of new theories, especially thanks to the new way of approaching them.

Thus, although any profound learning may be useful to a teacher in one way or another, the essential thing is that he should know not particular axiomatic systems but the different ways of axiomatizing and of conducting deduction. From the psychological point of view, the effort he must make to adapt to different points of view, to adopt new symbols and a new vocabulary, will enable him to realize better what he is requiring of the pupils and what is giving them trouble. Moreover, he will understand better the plan chosen by the textbook: he will be able to justify or modify it in accord with the reactions of his class; he will be able to seek the comparisons and similarities that clarify a mathematical situation; he will know that there are real difficulties and will know how to go around them when it is too hard to go over them. He will not have a guilty conscience if he appeals to intuition when he judges it useful, when it would be unreasonable or wrong to arouse doubt or fear in his pupils. On the question of functions without derivatives, Lebesgue notes: "One could maintain, and not without the appearance of reason, that these researchers were in some way depressing; that they were a school of doubt and not of action; that instead of saying to the young people ready to advance with ardor, 'the ground seems safe but watch out, because actually there are obstacles and precipices everywhere,' it would have been preferable to be able to say, 'where you see only obstacles and precipices, I am going to show you a safe route.' " To reconcile such advice with the progressive requirements of vigor and initiation into theories more and more general—that is certainly a large part of the pedagogic art. Cardinal Richelieu observed that "the problem of politics is to make possible the things that are necessary"; the art of pedagogy is to make comprehensible and reassuring the things that are necessary.

We have the inestimably good fortune to be living during a great renewal of mathematical thought—most simple, elementary and accessible. It is virtually impossible for most of us to make contact with the pure research of science today, because of lack of knowledge, lack of time, perhaps lack of talent or genius; but as teachers of mathematics we *can* establish a form of contact, for science and the thoughts of scientists are turning toward our area. At last we have a mathematics accessible to all! In a note on the great Ampère, who, as inspector-general, guided the work and "stimulated the intellectual activities of his subordinates by talking to them about philosophy or the classification of the sciences," Lebesgue says: "It is a difficult and never-settled problem to know how to help secondary-school science teachers find, in the science that they have studied and whose rudiments they teach, food for their own thought. How can we bring it about that their intellectual life will not separate itself from their profession, not become opposed to it, and that they may accomplish their task with more joy and pride and, incidentally, more effectiveness?"

The problem is now resolved; it is up to each of us to pursue the solution. It would be denying our mission not to profit from the breath of fresh air that is offered to us, not to find again the enthusiasm of youth, for we are invited to the work of reviewing values, as mathematics, ever more useful and fertile, is clothing itself in a new aspect of youth and beauty.

GLOSSARY OF SYMBOLS

Logic

⇒	"implies"
⇔	"is equivalent to"
∧	"and"
∨	"or"
∀	"for all" (universal quantifier)
∃	"there exists at least one"

Theory of sets

∈	"belongs to" or "is a member of"
∉	"does not belong to" or "is not a member of"
⊃	"includes"
⊆	"is included in" or "is a subset of"
⊂	"is properly included in" or "is a proper subset of"
∪	"union"
∩	"intersection"
CA	"the complement of A"
∅	"the null set" or "the empty set"

Mappings and functions

↳	"gives" or "has for an image" or "is transformed into" (passage from an element to its image)
↳ᴬ	Passage by the mapping A
↳ᶠ	Passage by means of the function f
↳ᵀ	Passage by the transformation T
→	"tends toward" or "has for a limit"

APPENDICES

EXAMPLES OF THE
APPLICATIONS OF LOGIC

We have indicated how important it is, from the pedagogic point of view, to present the meaning of a theorem with precision, and to recognize it under the various forms that its statement may take. This is not so obvious to pupils, especially if the statement contains quantifiers. Formalizing the statement is the only means of assuring precision of thought, because in formalization there is an obligation to use only a small number of symbols which are completely defined.

Examples of Statements with Quantifiers

Example 1. We are discussing parallelograms P and their symmetries S with respect to a line. Let S(P) be the image of P. The sign $\equiv$ signifies the superposition of figures.

(1) $[\text{P is a rectangle}] \Rightarrow \left[\exists\,S,\ S(P) \equiv P \right]$

The contrapositive statement is:

(1') $\left[\forall S,\ S(P) \not\equiv P \right] \Rightarrow \left[\text{P is not a rectangle} \right]$

The converse statement is false; under the form contradictory to (1) it would be:

(2) $$\left[\text{P is not a rectangle}\right] \Rightarrow \left[\forall S,\ S(P) \not\equiv P\right]$$

and under the contradictory (1′), the contrapositive of (2) is:

(2′) $$\left[\exists S,\ S(P) \equiv P\right] \Rightarrow \left[\text{P is a rectangle}\right]$$

We see that the contradictory of a proposition is formed by changing the quantifier and taking the negation of the conclusion.

Example 2. Similarly, if we deal with integers, the double statement:

$$\left[p \text{ is even}\right] \Leftrightarrow \left[\exists k,\ p = 2k\right]$$

is equivalent to the double statement:

$$\left[p \text{ is odd}\right] \Leftrightarrow \left[\forall k,\ p \neq 2k\right]$$

Example 3. Consider the trinomials $f(x) = x^2 + px + q$ on the set of real numbers. Let $D = p^2 - 4q$

The double theorem:

(1) $$\left[D < 0\right] \Leftrightarrow \left[\forall x,\ f(x) > 0\right]$$

is equivalent to its contrapositive:

(1′) $$\left[D \geqq 0\right] \Leftrightarrow \left[\exists x,\ f(x) \leqq 0\right]$$

But we can also show that:

(2) $$\left[D \geqq 0\right] \Leftrightarrow \left[\exists x,\ f(x) = 0\right]$$

(3) $$\left[D = 0\right] \Leftrightarrow \left[\forall x,\ f(x) \geqq 0\right]$$

$$(4) \qquad \left[D > 0 \right] \Leftrightarrow \left[\exists x, f(x) < 0 \right]$$

Naturally, (4) can be further broken down, since its right-hand member is a conjunction of statements.

There exist two numbers x' and x'' such that:

$$f(x') = 0, \qquad f(x'') = 0$$

$$\left[x \in \,]x', x''[\, \right] \Leftrightarrow \left[f(x) < 0 \right]$$

$$\left[x \in \mathbf{C}[x', x''] \right] \Leftrightarrow \left[f(x) > 0 \right]$$

(Recall that $]x', x''[$ is the open interval $x' < x < x''$, and $[x', x'']$ is the closed interval $x' \leqq x \leqq x''$; $\mathbf{C}$ designates the complement.)

When students use any of these theorems, it is desirable to have them expressed exactly and completely; too often it is believed that students need only state the theorem and its converse.

Example 4. Let $F(x, y)$ be a function of two real variables. The definition of an absolute minimum is:

$$\left[F(x_0, y_0) \text{ is a minimum} \right] \Leftrightarrow \left[\forall x \text{ and } \forall y, \, F(x, y) \geqq F(x_0, y_0) \right]$$

from which we get the contrapositive statement:

$$\left[F(x_0, y_0) \text{ is not a minimum} \right] \Leftrightarrow \left[\exists x \text{ or } \exists y, \, F(x, y) < F(x_0, y_0) \right]$$

Example 5. Let $y = f(x)$ be a numerical function of one real variable. The definition of continuity is:

$$\left[f(x) \text{ is continuous} \right] \Leftrightarrow$$

$$\left[\forall \epsilon > 0, \, \exists \eta > 0, \, \{ \forall x, \, |x - x_0| < \eta \Rightarrow |y - y_0| < \epsilon \} \right]$$

From this we get the contrapositive statement (the double statement of an implication and its converse, since it is a question of a defining property):

$$\Big[f(x) \text{ is not continuous} \Big] \Leftrightarrow$$

$$\Big[\forall \eta > 0, \ \exists \epsilon > 0, \ \{ \exists x, \ |x - x_0| < \eta \Rightarrow |y - y_0| > \epsilon \} \Big]$$

In what follows we will present the condition of existence under a different form. If there are elements in the domain which satisfy the conjunction of hypotheses, we will say that the conjunction is realizable and we will designate it by using the abbreviation r. In the contrary case, the unrealizable conjunction will be indicated by the symbol ur.

Consider a property P and its negation P'. For every element e of the domain E, any properties that will be considered will be supposed to be true (t) or false (f) without any ambiguity, so that for any element e:

$$\Big[\text{P is true} \Big] \Leftrightarrow \Big[\text{P' is false} \Big]$$

The conditional, $P_1 \Rightarrow P_2$, signifies, naturally, that every element e for which P_1 is true, will also give the value "true" for P_2. We will return to the tables (matrices) which we utilized in Chapter IV, but from a different point of view since we will be introducing an arbitrary number of properties P for which the twofold tables are not appropriate.

A. Let us first review the simple cases already studied:

Conditional: $P_1 \Rightarrow P_2$, with [P_1 is true] realizable:

Table (t_1)

P_1	P_2	
t	t	r
t	f	ur

Contrapositive: $P'_2 \Rightarrow P'_1$, with [P'_2 is true] realizable:

Table (t'_2)

P'_1	P'_2	
t	t	r
f	t	ur

that is to say:

Table (t_2)

P_1	P_2	
f	f	ur
t	f	r

The two tables are not identical. In order that we might be able to deduce the first line of (t_2) from (t_1), it is necessary to know that P'_2 is realizable, and this is sufficient; similarly, in order that we may be able to deduce the first line of (t_1) from (t_2) it is necessary and sufficient to know that P_1 is realizable. Finally, to avoid all difficulty, we will assume for all the considered properties the condition of *independent realizability:*

Table (r)

P	
t	r
f	r

Example: In the domain E we have the right triangle ABC; A is the right angle. Let AM be a median. We might have been able to prove that:

$$\left[(P_1),\ \angle B = \angle C \right] \Rightarrow \left[(P_2),\ BC = 2AM \right]$$

But the contrapositive statement is not acceptable because P'_2 is not realizable. The theorem which we have proved, "in an isosceles right triangle the hypotenuse is twice the median to it," would not be qualified as effective because (P'_1) $\Rightarrow$ (P_2) is also a true relation, since P_2 is true for all elements of the domain.

Finally, a theorem will be said to be effective if it corresponds to the table (T), which contains within it (t_1) and (t_2) and represents $P_1 \Rightarrow P_2$

	P_1	P_2	
	t	t	r
(T)	t	f	ur
	f	f	r

The converse theorem corresponds to $P_2 \Rightarrow P_1$

	P_1	P_2	
	t	t	r
(T_r)	f	t	ur
	f	f	r

The complete study of the dependence of the two properties P_1 and P_2 should be translatable by tables with four rows and not three. We meet with two types, depending on whether or not the conditions are equivalent.

(a) P_1 being true is *sufficient* (S) to make P_2 true, but it is not *necessary* (NS):

$$P_1 \Rightarrow P_2$$

	P_1	P_2		
	t	t	r	
(S)	t	f	ur	$\leftarrow$
	f	t	r	
	f	f	r	

(b) P_1 and P_2 are equivalent. Each is both necessary and sufficient for the other.

	P_1	P_2		
	t	t	r	
(NS)	t	f	ur	$\leftarrow$
	f	t	ur	$\leftarrow$
	f	f	r	

The often-used, vague and even improper phrase "state the converse" means: "having obtained table (T), determine the third rows of tables (S) and (NS) to find which of the two cases is correct."

B. Let us now consider the case in which P_1 is the conjunction of the p hypotheses:

$$P_1 \equiv [H_1 \wedge H_2 \wedge \cdots \wedge H_k \wedge \cdots \wedge H_p]$$

We will compare the two partially contrapositive statements:

$$\left[H_1 \wedge H_2 \wedge \cdots \wedge H_k \wedge \cdots \wedge H_p\right] \Rightarrow P_2$$

and
$$\left[H_1 \wedge H_2 \wedge \cdots \wedge P_2' \wedge \cdots \wedge H_p\right] \Rightarrow H_k$$

The equivalence of these two statements results from the equivalence of the contrapositive statements studied in (A) above, for we merely have to consider as a domain E_k, the subset of E made up of the elements for which all hypotheses H_i, except possibly H_k, are "true." But we must assume appropriate conditions of independent realizability: in order that $k + 1$ statements be equivalent, it is necessary that the two values "t" and "f" be attributable in all possible ways to p of the $p + 1$ properties which arise.

Finally, as the $p + 1$ properties will play analogous roles, we will change the notation and call them, in the sequel, $P_1, P_2, \cdots, P_{p+1}$; but we will limit ourselves to three properties—which is sufficient for most elementary statements. We will characterize as the *normal case* the conjunction of three tables of realization analogous to:

	P_i	P_j	
	t	t	r
$(r_{i,j})$	t	f	r
	f	t	r
	f	f	r

(i, j) being $(1, 2)$ or $(2, 3)$ or $(1, 3)$

The three equivalent statements:

$$\left[P_1 \wedge P_2\right] \Rightarrow P_0, \quad \left[P_3' \wedge P_2\right] \Rightarrow P_1', \quad \left[P_1 \wedge P_3'\right] \Rightarrow P_2'$$

are then represented by the table ($s_{1,2}$), which needs to be completed by supplying the four missing rows:

	P_1	P_2	P_3	
	t	t	t	r
$s_{1,2}$	t	t	f	ur
	t	f	f	r
	f	t	f	r

But we can already state that there are theorems of great interest which will not be the normal case; we will say that they correspond to composite tables and we will demonstrate this in the sequel.

C. *Examples of the normal case.* The tables ($r_{i,j}$) are assumed to be correct.

(1) *Three theorems*, therefore nine equivalent forms of statement.
Example: Consider the symmetries of a plane figure. Two lines x and y are perpendicular to each other at the point O.

P_1: symmetry with respect to x;

P_2: symmetry with respect to y;

P_3: symmetry with respect to O.

Three theorems:

$$\left[P_1 \wedge P_2 \right] \Rightarrow P_3 \text{ (three forms)};$$

$$\left[P_2 \wedge P_3 \right] \Rightarrow P_1 \text{ (three forms)};$$

$$\left[P_3 \wedge P_1 \right] \Rightarrow P_2 \text{ (three forms)}. \quad \text{[See table (N}_3\text{)}$$

(2) *Two theorems*, therefore six equivalent forms.
Example: Given in a plane P, a straight line D, a point K on D and a point H not on D. A point A not on plane P.

P_1: AH perpendicular to plane P;

P_2: AK perpendicular to line D;

P_3: HK perpendicular to line D.

The theorems:

$$\left[P_1 \wedge P_2 \right] \Rightarrow P_3 \text{ (three forms);}$$

$$\left[P_1 \wedge P_3 \right] \Rightarrow P_2 \text{ (three forms).} \quad [\text{See table } (N_2)]$$

Another example: Convex quadrilaterals ABCD

P_1: AB ∥ CD

P_2: AD ∥ BC

P_3: AB = CD

Another example: Given angle xAy and its orthogonal projection $x'A'y'$ on a plane p.

P_1: Ax ∥ p

P_2: Angle xAy is right

P_3: Angle $x'A'y'$ is right.

Let us observe that the table would be (N_3) and not (N_2) if P_1 were replaced by a less precise condition, namely, one side parallel to p.

Table (N_3)

P_1	P_2	P_3		
t	t	t	r	
t	t	f	ur	←
t	f	t	ur	←
f	t	t	ur	←
f	f	t	r	
f	t	f	r	
t	f	f	r	
$\int$	$\int$	$\int$	$\imath$	

Table (N_2)

P_1	P_2	P_3		
t	t	t	r	
t	t	f	ur	←
t	f	t	ur	←
f	t	t	r	
f	f	t	r	
f	t	f	r	
t	f	f	r	
$\int$	$\int$	$\int$	$\imath$	

(3) *A single theorem*, therefore three forms.

Example: Given six points such that $\angle AOB = \angle A'O'B'$

$$P_1: OA = O'A'$$

$$P_2: OB = O'B'$$

$$P_3: AB = A'B'$$

A single theorem:

$$\left[P_1 \wedge P_2 \right] \Rightarrow P_3 \text{ (three forms)}.$$

Table (N_1)

P_1	P_2	P_3		
t	t	t	r	
t	t	f	ur	$\leftarrow$
t	f	t	r	
f	t	t	r	
f	f	t	r	
f	t	f	r	
t	f	f	r	
f	f	f	r	

Another example: The second example of the previous case if we omit the word "convex."

D. *Examples of compound tables.* These correspond to a ternary theorem and one or two binary theorems. These are the only cases if we consider only "effective" theorems.

(1) *A single binary theorem.*

Example: a, b, d are integers.

$$P_1: d \text{ is a divisor of } ab;$$

$$P_2: d \text{ is relatively prime to } a;$$

$$P_3: d \text{ is a divisor of } b.$$

Ternary theorem:

$$\left[P_1 \wedge P_2 \right] \Rightarrow P_3 \text{ (three forms)}$$

Binary theorem:

$$P_3 \Rightarrow P_1 \text{ (two forms).}$$

Table (C₁)

P₁	P₂	P₃		
t	*t*	*t*	*r*	
t	*t*	*f*	*ur*	←
t	*f*	*t*	*r*	
f	*t*	*t*	*ur*	←
f	*f*	*t*	*ur*	←
f	*t*	*f*	*r*	
t	*f*	*f*	*r*	
f	*f*	*f*	*r*	

We see that $(r_{1,2})$ and $(r_{2,3})$ appear in C_1 but $(r_{1,3})$ does not. Here we find table $(\gamma_{1,3})$ in which, in each case, the second column can be either *t* or *f*:

Table (γ₁,₃)

P₁	P₂	P₃	
t		*t*	*r*
f		*t*	*ur*
f		*f*	*r*

(2) *Two binary theorems.*

Example: Given two non-parallel lines x and y in a plane p, and a plane p':

$$P_1: p' \parallel x$$

$$P_2: p' \parallel y$$

$$P_3: p' \parallel p$$

Ternary theorem: $\left[P_1 \wedge P_2 \right] \Rightarrow P_3$ (three forms)

First binary theorem: $\quad P_3 \Rightarrow P_1$ (two forms)

Second binary theorem: $\quad P_3 \Rightarrow P_2$ (two forms)

Table (C$_2$)

P_1	P_2	P_3		
t	t	t	r	
t	t	f	ur	$\leftarrow$
t	f	t	ur	$\leftarrow$
f	t	t	ur	$\leftarrow$
f	f	t	ur	$\leftarrow$
f	t	f	r	
t	f	f	r	
f	f	f	r	

The table $(r_{1,2})$ is contained in (C$_2$) but $(r_{2,3})$ and $(r_{1,3})$ are not. We can find in (C$_2$) the two tables which represent binary theorems.

NOTE: We notice again, by our tables, that the conditional is transitive:

	$P_1 \Rightarrow P_2$				$P_2 \Rightarrow P_3$	
P_1	P_2			P_2	P_3	
t	t	r	and	t	t	r
t	f	ur		t	f	ur
f	f	r		f	f	r

These two tables are equivalent to:

P_1	P_2	P_3	
t	t	t	r
t	t	f	ur
t	f	t	ur
f	t	t	
f	f	t	
f	t	f	ur
t	f	f	ur
f	f	f	r

which contains

P_1	P_3	
t	t	r
t	f	ur
f	f	r

SECOND NOTE: Venn diagrams can be used in all these cases. We first consider the conditions of independent realizability by stating that the closed-line boundary whose interior gives, for instance, the value "t" to P_i divides every region bounded by the other lines into two regions. We prove that this is possible by mathematical induction (it is sufficient to number the regions in such a way that two consecutive regions have a boundary in common, which then directs the next line to be traced). For p properties, there are therefore 2^p regions—as many as there are rows in the tables.

We deduce the images of the desired tables by making regions disappear by superposing certain arcs of curves. We shall not draw these diagrams as they do not seem very practical.

Let us conclude by emphasizing the great variety of structures that the important theorems of elementary mathematics display—a variety which is often hidden by the very similar verbal forms under which they appear in general. We see also that for a theorem that is even a little bit complicated, the phrase "and conversely" has no precise meaning: it must be determined by stating with precision just exactly what one wishes to prove.

AN EXAMPLE OF THE
USE OF FORMALISM:
THE THEOREMS OF SIMSON,
MIQUEL, AND CLIFFORD

If we look at mathematics from the outside as something already finished, we are likely to think of formalism as a method of exposition without any psychological bonds with research and creation. The only advantages we see in it then are the avoidance of having ideas submerged under a verbal flood and the clarification of their structure. This last is what justifies formalism as a language well adapted to mathematical exposition insofar as it is logical. However, there are many research men, creators, who assure us that they have found a method of discovery in formalism. The analogy of formalism in two areas of research permits the consideration of the two areas as *models* of a single structure, so that the experience acquired in one of the areas serves in the exploration of the other.

Each model carries with it not only the structure which is being studied and which it has in common with the other model, but also other structures which are characteristic of itself; therefore, not every property of a model is usable in the investigation. (Consider, for instance, the models of organic molecules or those of Bohr's atom;

they would give a dangerously erroneous image if we took them for enlargements of reality!)

We shall try to suggest this role of the model and of formalism by considering an elementary exercise. We will be excused, we hope, if we do not give an example of a discovery! We hope, however, to indicate how the method might become a trek towards the unexplored if it were undertaken by a mathematician worthy of it.

Point of Departure

Consider a figure (F) made up of a set of four points A, B, C, D. Let us call the three sides emanating from a point, a, b, c (for example A = $a \cap b \cap c$) and let a', b', c' be the opposite sides respectively. The condition of the inscriptibility of A, B, C, D can be translated— depending on the choice of labels for the lines—by one or the other of the equalities (or rather congruences) of angles:

(1) $$(a, b) + (a', b') = 0 \pmod \pi$$

(2) $$(b, c) + (b', c') = 0 \pmod \pi$$

The theorem of Chasles enables us to deduce from this the following four additional equalities (to within π):

(3) $$(a, c) + (a', c') = 0$$

(4) $$(a, b') + (a', b) = 0$$

(5) $$(a, c') + (a', c) = 0$$

(6) $$(b, c') + (b', c) = 0$$

If these equalities are true for three pairs of lines no three of which are concurrent (Figure F') they express the conditions of inscriptibility of three sets of four points:

$$a \cap b, \quad a' \cap b', \quad a \cap b', \quad a' \cap b$$
$$b \cap c, \quad b' \cap c', \quad b \cap c', \quad b' \cap c$$
$$c \cap a, \quad c' \cap a', \quad c \cap a', \quad c' \cap a$$

We know that this can be expressed by saying that the three pairs of lines are anti-parallel, two by two.

We wish to construct another model of this structure in order to make more intuitive and more obvious in a diagram that which does not appear clearly in the figures (F) and (F′) and their circles (which we have not drawn).

The relation:

$$(a, b) + (a', b') = 0 \ (\text{mod } \pi)$$

which expresses the inscriptibility, suggests the relation

$$\overrightarrow{ab} + \overrightarrow{a'b'} = 0$$

between vectors, which expresses the sameness of direction of the vectors $\overrightarrow{ab}$ and $\overrightarrow{b'a'}$. Now, the only *operation* that we have used on the angles (mod π) is the one expressed by the formula of Chasles, a formula which has the same form for vectors. A new figure (f) can be formed, made up of points which are the images of a, b, a', b', etc. But we need to construct a configuration such that the system of equalities, which we will write now in an ambiguous form as:

(1) $$ab + a'b' = 0$$

and

(2) $$bc + b'c' = 0$$

should imply the equalities (3), (4), (5), (6). This configuration is given by *symmetry with respect to a point*, say in a plane.

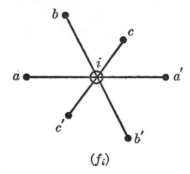

(f_i)

We thus get the fundamental figure (f_i) of inscriptibility (i). If we assume, moreover: $a \cap b \cap c = A$, we shall have *one* circle (i). Otherwise, if all the intersections, such as $a \cap b \cap c$, $a \cap b \cap c'$, are empty, we shall have three circles (i).

We see that the figure (f_i) is determined if we choose, for instance, a, b, c, a'. Since the center of symmetry i is defined by $ai = ia'$, this point should be considered as the image in (f) of the set of bisectors of the opposite angles (a, a'); (b, b'); (c, c') of F. We can already see how different are the separate individual structures of the two models, over and beyond the structure they have in common. In particular, we cannot translate, for example, the relation of perpendicularity in (F) without ascribing to (f) an equivalence relation between certain points such that $2ab = 0$, with a and b distinct. We will not do this, so that we shall be able to get in (F) only general figures.

Application

Theorem I—Let us put side by side two figures, f_i. Let the schema be (f_I).

The vectorial equalities are obvious:

$$1\,2 + 1'\,2' = 2\,i_1\,i_2 = I \quad III$$

If we complete the figure by putting in the inscriptibilities i_3 and i_4 we shall have:

$$1\,2 + 1'\,2' = 4\,3 + 4'\,3'$$

and therefore:

$$[1\,2 = 4\,3] \Leftrightarrow [1'\,2' = 4'\,3']$$

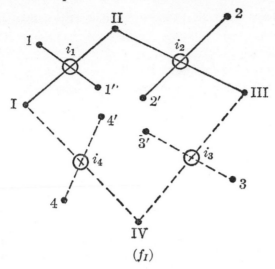

(f_1)

Interpretation in F. Four circles C_1, C_2, C_3, C_4 taken in cyclic order intersect each other in A, A'; B, B'; C, C'; D D'. (A A' the radical axis of C_1 and C_2 is represented by I and the chord A B by 1, etc.). The condition for the inscriptibility of A, B, C, D brings about the inscriptibility of A', B', C', D'. (That is, A', B', C', D' *are inscriptible if and only if* A, B, C, D *are inscriptible.*)

Theorem II—Theorem of Simson (generalized for any angle).

Description in F. Three non-collinear points A, B, C form a triangle with sides a, b, c. Let the point M be connected to A, B, C by the lines α, β, γ and to three points A', B', C' taken on a, b, c by the lines α', β', γ'. Let $a' = B'C'$, $b' = A'C'$, $c' = A'B'$.

It should be observed that $(a', b') = 0 \pmod{\pi}$ implies $(b', c') = 0 \pmod{\pi}$.

Let us study the figure in the case where:

$$(\text{H}) \quad (a, \alpha') = (b, \beta') = (c, \gamma'), \pmod{\pi}$$

Translation in (f).

Given: Four arbitrary points a, b, c, α'. The points a', b', c' such that no two of them are coincident or they are all three coincident.

Hypothesis (H): $a\alpha' = b\beta' = c\gamma'$ (the vector equalities, as we said).

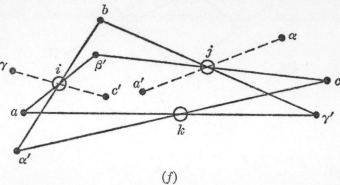

(f)

We see the inscriptibilities (i), (j), (k) and we complete the figure with the pair c', γ for (i) and a', α for (j), following the schema (f_i) above. We *see* immediately from the figure that $a'c' = 0$ is equivalent to $\gamma\alpha = ac$ as well as equal to $2ij$, which expresses the inscriptibility of:

$$\mathrm{M} = \alpha \cap \gamma, \quad \mathrm{B} = a \cap c, \quad \mathrm{A} = a \cap \alpha, \quad \mathrm{C} = c \cap \gamma$$

From which we get the usual statement about the figure (F): *The points* A, B, C, M *are inscriptible if and only if* A', B', C' *are collinear.*

If the points a', b', c' are coincident in, say, d (the Simson line) we obtain the figure (f_s):

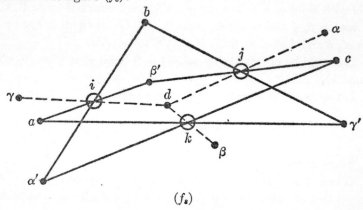

(f_s)

(1) From this we deduce two classical results: Let us fix a, b, c, α' (therefore i, k, γ', β', j are also determined), but let α vary so that α becomes α_1; then d becomes d_1 and $\alpha\alpha' = -dd_1$. From this we get the theorem: "If the point M describes the circle ABC, its Simson line turns through an angle which is opposite to the angle through which the chords AM, BM, CM turn."

If we now interpret $db = -\alpha\gamma'$ as the inscriptibility of:

$$A = d \cap b, \quad C = b \cap \gamma', \quad M = \gamma' \cap \alpha, \quad A_1 = d \cap \alpha$$

we get the theorem: "The line parallel to the Simson line through the point A meets the line MA' on the circle."

(2) *A more general interpretation of the figure (f_s).*

Let us use a figure of the type (F_i^7) rather than (F_i), that is, let us no longer suppose that the six lines α, β, γ, α', β', γ' are concurrent in M. Let us take any a, b, c, α' and then let us take β' and γ' so that they satisfy (H), and let us consider:

$$M_c = \alpha' \cap \beta', \quad M_a = \beta' \cap \gamma', \quad M_b = \gamma' \cap \alpha'$$

from which we get the three circles:

$$AB'C'M_a, \quad BC'A'M_b, \quad CA'B'M_c$$

The lines a', b', c' are still B'C', C'A', A'B', but the lines α, β, γ (that is, AM_a, BM_b, CM_c) determine the points:

$$N_a = \beta \cap \gamma, \quad N_b = \alpha \cap \gamma, \quad N_c = \alpha \cap \beta$$

The condition of collinearity of A', B', C' is still given by $\gamma\alpha = ac$; here it expresses the fact that N_b is on the circle ABC. Similarly, N_c is on this circle. Therefore these points coincide at a point N different from A in which α intersects (ABC). And N_a is also at N. Hence the theorem: "If a line cuts the sides a, b, c of a triangle ABC in A', B', C', respectively, the three lines α', β', γ' drawn through A', B', C' and satisfying (H) determine a triangle $M_aM_bM_c$ such that AM_a, BM_b, CM_c are concurrent at a point N of the circle (ABC). The two triangles are similar and homologic, and they play the same role, in that N is also on the circle circumscribed about the second triangle."

Theorems of Miquel and Clifford (with n lines)

Let us return to the interpretation of (f_s) by means of the theorem of Simson. We can state the theorem in a form such that the four lines play the same role:

(E_4) *Given four lines, the four circles about the resulting triangles are concurrent in a point.*

We use the following notation to prepare for the generalization:

Let the lines be designated by the numerals 1, 2, 3, 4.

Let the points of order 2 be indicated so that, e.g., $1 \cap 2$ is written as M(1 2).

Let the circles of order 3 be indicated by, e.g., C(1 2 3).

Let the point of concurrence of order 4 be written, M(1 2 3 4).

Consider the case $n = 5$.

Let $(1\ 2)^5$ be the line M(1 2) M(1 2 3 4)
and $((4\ 5))$ be the line M(1 2 3 5) M(1 2 3 4)

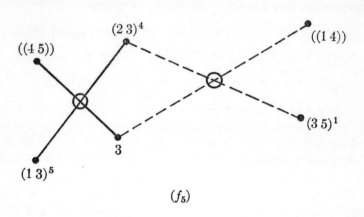

(f_5)

Considering the two circles C(1 2 3) and C(2 3 5) we obtain the schema (f_5) in which we see:

$$((4\ 5))\ ((1\ 4)) = (1\ 3)^5\ (3\ 5)^1$$

Now in the definition of the right-hand side of this equation, 2 and 4 play the same role; therefore:

$$((4\ 5))\ ((1\ 4)) = ((2\ 5))\ ((2\ 4))$$

which expresses the inscriptibility of:

$$M(1\ 2\ 3\ 4), \quad M(1\ 2\ 3\ 5), \quad M(2\ 3\ 4\ 5), \quad M(1\ 3\ 4\ 5)$$

Similarly, $M(1\ 2\ 4\ 5)$ is on this circle. Hence we get:

(E_5) *Given five lines, the five points of theorem* (E_4) *are concyclic* (*Theorem of Miquel*). This circle, of order 5, shall be designated by $C(1\ 2\ 3\ 4\ 5)$.

The General Theorem of Clifford [*] To every set of $n = 2k$ points we can associate a point $M(1, 2, \cdots, 2k)$, and to every set of $n = 2k + 1$ lines we can associate a circle $C(1, 2, \cdots, 2k + 1)$ such that every point M of order n lies on every circle of order $n - 1$, if the set of indices of the circle is included in the set of indices of the point; and also on every circle of order $n + 1$, if the set of indices of the circle contains the set of indices of the point.

The theorem is clearly true for the case $n = 5$. The investigation can be pursued by a simple examination of the indices: the symbolism we have adopted will itself give the demonstration.

$n = 6$. Consider the four circles with their intersections:

$$C(2\ 3\ 4\ 5) \cap C(2\ 5\ 6) \qquad = M(2\ 4\ 5\ 6) \cup M(2\ 3\ 5\ 6)$$

$$C(2\ 5\ 6) \quad \cap C(1\ 5\ 6) \qquad = M(5\ 6) \qquad \cup M(1\ 2\ 5\ 6)$$

$$C(1\ 5\ 6) \quad \cap C(1\ 3\ 4\ 5\ 6) = M(1\ 4\ 5\ 6) \cup M(1\ 3\ 5\ 6)$$

$$C(1\ 4\ 5\ 6) \cap C(2\ 3\ 4\ 5\ 6) = M(3\ 4\ 5\ 6) \cup Q$$

The four points named first in the right-hand members of these equations are on $C(4\ 5\ 6)$, therefore (by theorem I) the three points of order 4 named second have in common the point Q. But this circle is $C(1\ 2\ 3\ 5\ 6)$. Therefore, the introduced three circles of order 5 are concurrent in Q. Permuting, for example, 3 and 4, we see that Q is also on $C(1\ 2\ 4\ 5\ 6)$ and similarly with the other circles of order 5;

[*] The idea of utilizing theorem I in the demonstration was suggested by H. Lebesgue in an assignment at the École Normale Supérieure of Sèvres.

therefore, *all the circles of order 5* are concurrent in a point of order 6 named M(1 2 3 4 5 6).

$n = 7$. Consider the four points of order 6:

C(3 4 5 6 7) ∩ C(1 4 5 6 7) = M(4 5 6 7) ∪ M(1 3 4 5 6 7)

C(1 4 5 6 7) ∩ C(1 2 5 6 7) = M(1 5 6 7) ∪ M(1 2 4 5 6 7)

C(1 2 5 6 7) ∩ C(2 3 5 6 7) = M(2 5 6 7) ∪ M(1 2 3 5 6 7)

C(2 3 5 6 7) ∩ C(3 4 5 6 7) = M(3 5 6 7) ∪ M(2 3 4 5 6 7)

Now, the four points named first are on C(5 6 7), therefore (by theorem I) the four named points of order 6 are on the circle passing through three of them. Therefore, *all the points of order 6 are on the same circle of order 7*, C(1 2 3 4 5 6 7).

$n \geqq 8$. The reasoning above in the cases $n = 6$ and $n = 7$ actually used only the indices 1, 2, 3, 4. It remains valid if we write, at the right of the set of indices, two, then four, then $\cdots$, additional indices. Then, by mathematical induction, the general theorem is proved.

Index

Index